KT-560-468

COUNTY STORE
MUSIC
11. NOV. 1980
-9. MAY 1985
17. APR. 1986
HAMPSHIRE COUNTY LIBRARY
WITHDRAWN.

THE ABDUCTION FROM THE SERAGLIO

DIE ENTFUEHRUNG AUS DEM SERAIL

Comic Opera in Three Acts

by

WOLFGANG AMADEUS MOZART

German original text by Bretzner, adapted by Stephanie the Younger

English translation by

RUTH *and* THOMAS MARTIN

(Revised Version)

VOCAL SCORE

$7.50

BOOSEY & HAWKES

CHARACTERS

Selim, Pasha .... *Speaking role*
Constanza, beloved of Belmonte .... *Soprano*
Blonda, maid of Constanza .... *Soprano*
Belmonte, a Spanish nobleman .... *Tenor*
Pedrillo, servant of Belmonte .... *Tenor*
Osmin, overseer of the country palace of the Pasha .... *Bass*
Klaas, a boatsman .... *Speaking role*
A Mute

Janissaries, Slaves, Guards.

PLACE: The country palace of the Pasha.

TIME: Middle of the 16th century.

INDEX

ACT I

ACT II

ACT III

DIE ENTFUEHRUNG AUS DEM SERAIL

THE ABDUCTION FROM THE SERAGLIO

Original text by Bretzner,
Adapted by Stephanie the Younger.
Revised English translation by
RUTH and THOMAS MARTIN

W. A. MOZART
COMPOSED 1782 IN VIENNA

OVERTURE

Printed in U.S.A.
U.S.Book No.109

f
p
f
p
p
f
f
p
f

Andante.
p
f
cresc.

Presto.

p
f
p
f
p
f
p
f
p
f
p

ERSTER AUFZUG

Platz vor dem Palast des Bassa am Ufer des Meeres.

Erster Auftritt

Belmonte (allein)

FIRST ACT

Square in front of the palace of the Pasha on the shore of the sea.

First Scene

Belmonte (alone)

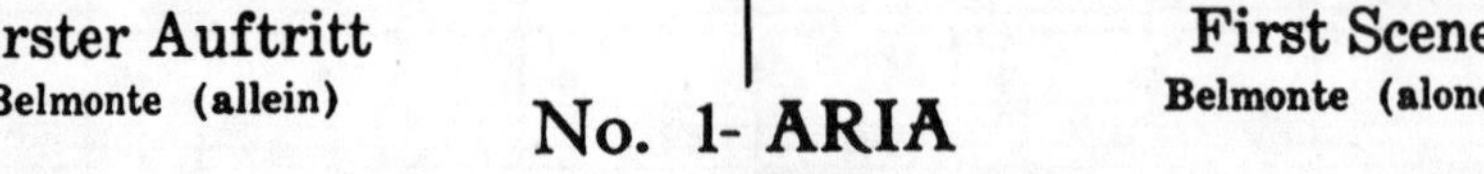

No. 1- ARIA

Andante.

B. Gieb mir da-für nun Freu-den, nun Freu-den, und brin-ge mich an's Ziel, und brin - ge mich an's Ziel.
Hope-fully I am waiting, Constanza, to bring you joy a - gain, to bring you joy a-gain.

Gieb mir da-für nun Freuden, nun Freuden, und bringe mich an's Ziel, und brin - - - - - ge mich an's Ziel, und brin - - ge mich, und brin-ge mich an's Ziel, und brin - - ge mich, und brin - - - - ge mich an's Ziel.
Hope-fully I am waiting, Constanza, to bring you joy a-gain, to bring - - - - - you joy a-gain, to bring - - you joy to bring you joy a-gain, to bring you joy - to bring - - - - you joy a-gain.

p mf p sf p sf p f p cresc. f p f

BELMONTE: Aber wie soll ich in den Palast kommen? Wie sie sehen? Wie sprechen?

BELMONTE: But how shall I gain entrance to the palace? How shall I see her? How speak to her?

Zweiter Auftritt

Belmonte. Osmin.

Osmin erscheint mit einer Leiter. Er lehnt sie an einen Feigenbaum vor dem Palast, steigt hinauf und nimmt Feigen ab.

Second Scene

Belmonte. Osmin.

Osmin appears with a ladder. He leans it against a fig-tree in front of the palace, climbs up and plucks figs.

No. 2 - SONG AND DUET

* Hey, my good man, do you hear? Is this Pasha Selim's palace?

O.
Treu-e gu-te Nacht, und dann Treu-e gu-te Nacht, gu-te Nacht! Tralla-
vir-tue say good-bye, or to vir-tue say good-bye, say good bye. Tralla-
pp
Allegro.
Belm.
O.
B.
le-ra, tral-la-le-ra, tral-la-le-ra, tral-la-le-ra. Verwünscht seist du sammt dei-nem
le-ra, tral-la-le-ra, tral-la-le-ra, tral-la-le-ra! The dev-il take you and your
cresc.
f
p
B.
Lie-de! ich bin dein Sin-gen nun schon mü-de, so hör' doch nur ein ein-zig'
sing-ing. I heard e-nough, my ears are ring-ing. One thing is all I want to
fp
fp
fp
Osm.
B.
O.
Wort! Was-Henker, lasst Ihr Euch ge-lü-sten, Euch zu er-ei-fern, Euch zu
know In de-vil's name why such a flus-ter? What causes you to boast and
f
p
O.
brüsten! was wollt Ihr? was wollt Ihr? was wollt Ihr? Hur-tig, ich muss fort!
bluster? What is it, what is it, what is it? Hur-ry, I must go,
f
sf
p

O.
B.
Belm.
Hur - tig, ich muss fort!
hur - ry, I must go!
Ist das des Bas-sa Se-lim
Is this where Pa-sha Se-lim
f
p
B.
Haus? Ist das des Bas-sa Se-lim Haus?
lives? Is this where Pa-sha Se-lim lives?
Osm.
(Wants to go.)
So wartet doch!
I want to know!
O.
He!
Eh!
Das ist des Bas - sa Se - lim Haus. (Will fort.) Ich kann nicht
This is where Pa-sha Se-lim lives. That is your
sfp
Ein Wort!
One word!
So wartet doch!
-before you go.
Ein Wort!
One word!
weilen, geschwind, denn ich muss eilen; ich kann nicht weilen, geschwind, denn ich muss
worry, be off I'm in a hurry, That is your worry! be off, I'm in a
Osm.
Belm.
ei-len.
hur-ry.
Seid Ihr in sei-nen Dien-sten, Freund? He! Seid Ihr in
Are you the Pa-sha's ser-vant, friend? Eh! Are you the
sei-nen Dien-sten, Freund? He! Seid Ihr in sei-nen Dien-sten, Freund? Ich bin in
Pa-sha's ser-vant, friend? Eh! Are you the Pa-sha's ser-vant, friend? I am the

Recit. Belm.
sei- nen Dien- sten. Freund!
Pa -sha's ser - vant, friend.
Wie kann ich den Pe-drill wohl
Then tell me where to find Pe-
Osm.
sprechen, der hier in sei-nen Diensten steht? Den Schurken. der den Hals soll brechen!
dril-lo. he must be work-ing here to-day. The scoun-drel, that re-pul-sive fellow?
a tempo
Seht selber zu, seht selber zu, wenn's anders geht, seht selber zu, wenn's anders
See for yourself, see for yourself, that's all I say, see for yourself, that's all I
(to himself) (to himself)
Belm. (für sich.) Osm. (für sich.) Belm.
geht! Was für ein al-ter grober Bengel! Das ist just so ein Galgen-schwengel, was für ein
say! O what a crank-y ugly duffer! He's just a-noth-er bra-zen bluf-fer. Of all the
al- ter gro-ber Ben-gel, was für ein al- ter gro-ber Ben-gel, was für ein al- ter gro-ber,
rude un-civ-il fel-lows, of all the rude un-civ il fel-lows, of all the rude un-civ-il
Osm.
das ist just so ein Gal- gen - schwengel, das ist just so ein Gal - gen - schwengel, das ist just
The man be-longs up-on the gal-lows, the man be-longs up-on the gal-lows, the man be-

(to Osmin)
(zu Osmin.)
B.
al - ter grober Bengel! Ihr irrt, Ihr irrt, Ihr irrt, es ist ein braver Mann.
rude un-civ-il fel-lows. Oh no, oh no, oh no, there is no finer chap
O.
so ein Galgen-schwengel!
longs upon the gal-lows!
So brav, so brav, so
So fine, so fine, so
sf p
f
p
f
brav. dass man ihn spiessen kann.
fine, he is not worth a rap.
Ihr müsst ihn wahr - lich nicht recht ken-nen, Ihr müsst ihn
It's very clear you do not know him, it's very
Recht gut, ich liess' ihn heut' ver-
Into the dun-geon I would
p
fp
fp
fp
wahr - lich nicht recht ken-nen, Ihr müsst ihn wahr - lich nicht recht ken-nen. Ihr müsst ihn
clear you do not know him, it's very clear you do not know him, it's very
brennen, recht gut, ich liess' ihn heut' ver - brennen, recht gut, ich liess' ihn heut' ver-
throw him, into the dun-geon I would throw him, into the dun-geon I would
fp
fp
fp
fp
wahr - lich nicht recht kennen.
clear you do not know him.
brennen, recht gut, ich liess' ihn heut' ver-brennen, heut', heut' liess' ich ihn ver-bren - nen.
throw him. in-to the dun-geon I would throw him, yes, yes, that's where I would throw him.
fp
fp
cresc.
f

B.
O.
Es ist für-wahr ein gu-ter Tropf. es ist für-wahr ein gu-ter
You do him wrong to wish him dead. He is a ver-y honest
Auf ei-nen Pfahl gehört sein Kopf,
I'd just as soon cut off his head,
p. f. p. f. p. f. p. f. p. f. p.
Tropf, es ist für-wahr ein gu-te
soul, he is a ver-y hon-est
auf ei-nen Pfahl gehört sein Kopf, auf ei-nen Pfahl gehört sein Kopf, auf ei-nen Pfahl gehört sein
his head be-longs up-on a pole, his head be-longs upon a pole, his head be-longs up-on a
f. p cresc.
Tropf, es ist für-wahr ein gu-ter Tropf, ein gu-ter
soul, he is a ver y hon-est soul. an hon-est
Kopf, auf ei-nen Pfahl gehört sein Kopf, auf ei-nen Pfahl gehört sein
pole, his head be-longs upon a pole, his head be-longs up-on a
fp fp
Tropf! So
soul Don't
Kopf, auf ei-nen Pfahl gehört sein Kopf, auf ei-nen Pfahl gehört sein Kopf! (will fort.)
pole, his head be-longs up-on a pole, his head be-longs up-on a pole (wants to go)
f p f fp fp

Osm.
Belm.
Osm.
bleibet doch. Was wollt Ihr noch? so bleibet doch! Was wollt Ihr was wollt Ihr, was
go a-way. Why should I stay? Don't go a way! Why should I, why should I, why
fp
f
wollt Ihr noch?
should I stay?
Belm.
Ich möchte ger - ne...
I'm only seek - ing ...
p
Osm. (spöttisch.)
(mockingly)
So hübsch von fer - ne um's Haus 'rum schleichen,
And sty-ly sneak - ing a-round the pa-lace,
und Mäd - chen stehlen? Fort, eu-res Gleichen braucht man hier nicht!
to steal a maiden? Go, we don't need your kind in this place!
sfp
Fort, fort, fort, fort, fort, eu-res Glei - chen braucht man hier
Go, go, go, go, go, we don't need your kind in this
cresc.

Belm.
B.
O.
Ihr seid be-ses-sen, sprecht vol-ler Gal-le mir so ver-mes-sen
You've lost your sen-ses thus to in-sult me and throw of-fen-ses
nicht!
place!
fp
in's A ge-sicht, mir so ver-mes-sen in's An-ge-sicht? Schont Euren
right in my face and throw of-fen-ses right in my face! Don't be so
Nur nicht in Ei-fer,
My time is precious,
Gei-fer, lasst Euer Droh'n. schont Euren Gei-fer, lasst Euer
vi-cious and change your tone. Don't be so vi-cious and change your
ich kenn' Euch schon, nur nicht in Ei-fer, ich kenn' Euch schon,
Leave me a-lone. My time is pre-cious. Leave me a-lone.
Droh'n, lasst Eu-er Droh'n, lasst Eu-er Droh'n!
tone. and change your tone, and change your tone.
ich kenn' Euch schon, ich kenn' Euch schon!
leave me a-lone, leave me a-lone!
tr
cresc.
p
f

Presto.
B.
O.
Marsch, geht zum Teufel! Ihr kriegt, ich schwöre, sonst oh-ne Gna-de die Basto - na-de; noch
Go to the devil, or I as-sure you, one hun-dred lash-es quick-ly will cure you. You
Presto.
fp
habt Ihr Zeit, noch habt Ihr Zeit!
still have time you still have time!
Es ist kein Zweifel, Ihr seid von Sinnen,
Your mad be- hav-ing shows you are rav-ing,
welch' ein Be - tragen auf meine Fragen! seid doch ge - scheid, gebt doch Be -
full of con- fu-sion, lost in de- lu-sion! What I have done, is not a
scheid!
crime!
Es ist kein Zweifel, Ihr seid von Sin - nen,
Your mad be-having shows you are rav-ing,
welch' ein Be-
full of con-
Marsch, geht zum Teu - fel! Ihr kriegt, ich schwö - re, sonst oh - ne Gna - de
Go to the de- vil, or I as-sure you, one hun-dred lash-es

B.
O.
tra - gen auf meine Fra - gen! gebt doch Be - scheid. gebt doch Be -
fu-sion lost in de-lu - sion! What I have done is not a
die Ba - sto - na - de; noch habt Ihr Zeit, noch
quick-ly will cure you you still have time, you
fp
scheid, gebt doch Be - scheid! Es ist kein Zwei-fel, Ihr seid von
crime, is not a crime! Your mad be-hav-ing shows you are
habt Ihr Zeit! Marsch, geht zum Teufel! Ihr kriegt, ich schwöre,
still have time! Go to the devil, or I as-sure you,
f
Sin - nen, welch' ein Be - tra - gen auf mei - ne Fra - gen! gebt doch Be -
rav - ing, full of con - fu-sion, lost in de - lu - sion! what I have
sonst oh - ne Gna - de die Ba - sto - na - de; noch habt Ihr Zeit,
one hun-dred lash-es quick-ly will cure you you still have time,
scheid, gebt doch Be - scheid, gebt doch Be - scheid,
done is not a crime, is not a crime.
noch habt Ihr Zeit, noch habt Ihr Zeit, noch habt Ihr
you still have time. be-gone, be-gone. you still have
p
cresc.

gebt doch Be-scheid, gebt doch Be-scheid, gebt doch Be-
is not a crime, is not a crime. What I have
Zeit, noch habt Ihr Zeit, noch habt Ihr Zeit,
time, you still have time, Be gone, be-gone
scheid, gebt doch Be-scheid, gebt doch Be-scheid, gebt
done is not a crime. is not a crime, is
noch habt Ihr Zeit, noch habt Ihr Zeit, noch
you still have time, you still have time, you
cresc.
doch Be-scheid, gebt doch Be scheid, gebt doch Be-scheid!
not a crime, is not a crime, not a crime!
habt Ihr Zeit, noch habt Ihr Zeit, noch habt Ihr Zeit!
still have time, you still have time, you still have time!
Osmin (drängt Belmonte hinaus). (pushes Belmonte out)

Dritter Auftritt

Osmin (allein). Hernach Pedrillo.

OSMIN: Könnt ich mir doch noch so einen Schurken auf die Nase setzen, wie den Pedrillo; so einen Gaudieb, der Tag und Nacht nichts tut, als nach meinen Weibern herumzuschleichen und zu schnobern, ob's nichts für seinen Schnabel setzt. Aber ich laure ihm sicher auf den Dienst, und wohl bekomm dir die Prügelsuppe, wenn ich dich einmal beim Kanthaken kriege! Hätt er sich nur beim Bassa nicht so eingeschmeichelt, er sollte den Strick längst um den Hals haben.
PEDRILLO: Nun, wie steht's, Osmin? Ist der Bassa noch nicht zurück?
OSMIN: Sieh darnach, wenn du's wissen willst.
PEDRILLO: Schon wieder Sturm im Kalender? Hast du das Gericht Feigen für mich gepflückt?
OSMIN: Gift für dich, verwünschter Schmarotzer?
PEDRILLO: Was in aller Welt ich dir nur getan haben muss, dass du beständig mit mir zankst. Lass uns doch einmal Friede machen.
OSMIN: Friede mit dir? Mit so einem schleichenden, spitzbübischen Passauf, der nur spioniert, wie er mir eins versetzen kann? Erdrosseln möcht ich dich!
PEDRILLO: Aber sag nur, warum, warum?
OSMIN: Warum? Weil ich dich nicht leiden kann.

Third Scene

Osmin (alone). Afterwards Pedrillo.

OSMIN: All I need is another rascal like that Pedrillo, who does nothing all day but prowl around the Harem! Had he not wheedled himself into the Pasha's favor, he would have had a rope around his neck long ago.
PEDRILLO: (enters) Well, how are you, Osmin? Has the Pasha returned?
OSMIN: Look for yourself, if you want to know.
PEDRILLO: Stormy weather again? Did you pick those figs for me?
OSMIN: Poison and daggers for you, confounded bloodhound! I would like to choke you!
PEDRILLO: But just tell me why?
OSMIN: Why? Because I don't like you!

nicht, mag ich für den Teu-fel nicht, mag ich für den Teu - fel
bide, tru-ly I can-not a-bide, tru - ly I can-not a - -
fp
fp
cresc.
nicht;
bide.
denn ihr gan-zes Thun und Lassen ist,
For their on-ly way of working is
f
fp
fp
uns auf den Dienst zu pas-sen, uns auf den Dienst zu
loaf-ing a-bout and lurk-ing, loaf-ing a- bout and
fp
fp
fp
ad lib.
pas-sen, doch mich trügt kein solch' Ge - sicht, doch mich
lurk-ing, but I... I am no one's fool, but I - -
fp
fp
f

Adagio.
Allegro.
trügt kein solch Ge-sicht. Eu-re Tücken, eu-re Rän-ke, eu-re Finten. eu-re
I am no one's fool. All your tricking, all your coaxing, all your cheating, all your
Schwänke sind mir ganz bekannt, sind mir ganz bekannt, sind mir ganz bekannt, ganz be-
hoax-ing, I know all too well, I know all too well, I know all too well, all too
kannt, sind mir ganz be-kannt. Mich zu hin-ter-gehen,
well, I know all too well. I de-fy your trap-ping.
müsst ihr früh auf-stehen, müsst ihr früh auf-ste-hen: ich hab' auch Ver-
You won't catch me nap-ping, you won't catch me nap-ping. No one tricks Os-
stand, ich hab' auch Ver-stand, ich hab' auch Ver-stand, ich!
min, no one tricks Os-min, no one tricks Os-min, No!

ich hab auch Ver - stand. Sol - che her - ge - lauf'ne Laf - - - - - - - - - - - - - fen, die nur nach den Wei - bern gaf - fen, mag ich
I am far too keen. All these good for noth - ing don - - - - - - - - - - - - - keys, lazy wom - an - chas - ing mon - keys, tru - ly
cresc.
für den Teu - fel nicht, mag ich für den Teufel nicht, mag ich für den Teu - fel
I can - not a - bide, tru - ly I cannot a - bide, tru - ly I can - not a -
cresc.
nicht; denn ihr gan - zes Thun und Las - sen ist, uns auf den Dienst zu
bide. For their on - ly way of working is loafing a - bout and
pas - sen, uns auf den Dienst zu pas - sen, doch mich trügt kein solch Ge -
lurk - ing, loafing a - bout and lurk - ing, but I-- I am no one's
ad lib.

Adagio.
Allegro.
O.
sicht, doch mich trügt kein solch Ge - sicht. Eu-re Tü-cken, eu-re Rän-ke, eu-re
fool. But I-- I am; no one's fool. All your tricking, all your coaxing, all your
f
fp
p
f
Fin-ten, eu-re Schwänke sind mir ganz be-kannt, sind mir ganz be-kannt,
cheating, all your hoax-ing, I know all too well, I know all too well,
p
sind mir ganz bekannt, ganz bekannt, sind mir ganz be-kannt Mich zu hin-ter-ge-hen,
I know all too well, all too well, I know all too well. I de-fy your trap ping,
sf
fp
müsst ihr früh auf - ste-hen, müsst ihr früh auf - ste-hen: ich hab auch Ver -
You won't catch me nap-ping, you won't catch me nap-ping. no one tricks Os-
stand, ich hab auch Ver - stand, ich hab auch Ver - stand, ich!
min. no one tricks Os-min, no one tricks Os-min, no!

ich hab' auch Ver-stand.
no one tricks Os-min--
ich hab' auch Ver - stand,
no one tricks Os - min,
ich hab' auch Ver - stand,
no one tricks Os-min,
ich hab' auch Ver - stand, ich!
no one tricks Os - min. No.
ich hab' auch Ver-stand,
I am far too keen,
ich hab' auch Ver-
I am far too
stand,
keen,
ich hab' auch Ver - stand.
I am far too keen.
Drum beim Bar-te des Pro-phe-ten! ich stu-die-re Tag und Nacht, dich so mit Ma-nier zu
But I'll work with con-cen-tra-tion, night and day and in be-tween, planning your as-sas-si-
p
cresc.
f

O.
töd-ten, nimm dich wie du willst in Acht; drum beim Bar-te des Pro-phe-ten! ich stu-die-re Tag und
na-tion or my name is not Os-min, but I'll work with concen tra tion night and day and in be-
f
p
Nacht, dich so mit Ma-nier, zu töd-ten, nimm dich wie du willst in Acht, nimm dich
tween, plan-ning your as-sas-si -na-tion, or my name is not Os min. Night and
sfp
wie du willst in Acht, nimm dich in Acht. nimm dich wie du willst in
day I'll stud-y hard, be on your guard, Night and day I'll stud-y
Acht, nimm dich in Acht, nimm dich wie du willst in Acht, nimm dich wie du willst in
hard. be on your guard, night and day I'll stud-y hard, night and day I'll stud-y
cresc.
Acht, nimm dich in Acht, nimm dich in Acht!
hard, be on your guard, be on your guard!

PEDRILLO: Was bist du für ein grausamer Kerl, und ich hab dir nichts getan.

OSMIN: Du hast ein Galgengesicht, das ist genug.

PEDRILLO: What a blood-thirsty fellow you are! And I never did you any harm.

OSMIN: You have the face of a gallows bird — that's enough!

Vierter Auftritt

Pedrillo (allein). Hernach **Belmonte.**

PEDRILLO. Geh nur, verwünschter Aufpasser; es ist noch nicht aller Tage Abend. Wer weiß, wer den andern überlistet; und dir mißtrauischem, gehässigem Menschenfeinde eine Grube zu graben, sollte ein wahres Fest für mich sein.

BELMONTE. Pedrillo, guter Pedrillo!

PEDRILLO. Ach mein bester Herr! Ist's möglich? Sind Sie's wirklich? Bravo, Madame Fortuna, bravo, das heißt doch Wort gehalten! Schon verzweifelte ich, ob einer meiner Briefe Sie getroffen hätte.

BELMONTE. Sag, guter Pedrillo, lebt meine Konstanze noch?

PEDRILLO. Lebt, und noch, hoff ich, für Sie. Seit dem schrecklichen Tage, an welchem das Glück uns einen so häßlichen Streich spielte und unser Schiff von den Seeräubern erobern ließ, haben wir mancherlei Drangsal erfahren. Glücklicherweise traf sich's noch, daß der Bassa Selim uns alle drei kaufte: Ihre Konstanze nämlich, meine Blonde und mich. Er ließ uns sogleich hier auf sein Landhaus bringen. Donna Konstanze ward seine auserwählte Geliebte.

BELMONTE. Ah! Was sagst du?

PEDRILLO. Nun, nur nicht so hitzig! Sie ist noch nicht in die schlimmsten Hände gefallen. Der Bassa ist ein Renegat und hat noch so viel Delikatesse, keine seiner Weiber zu seiner Liebe zu zwingen; und so viel ich weiß, spielt er noch immer den unerhörten Liebhaber.

BELMONTE. Wär es möglich? Wär Konstanze noch treu?

PEDRILLO. Sicher noch, lieber Herr! Aber wie's mit meinem Blondchen steht, weiß der Himmel! Das arme Ding schmachtet bei einem alten häßlichen Kerl, dem sie der Bassa geschenkt hat; und vielleicht – ach, ich darf gar nicht dran denken!

BELMONTE. Doch nicht der alte Kerl, der soeben ins Haus ging?

PEDRILLO. Eben der.

BELMONTE. Und dies ist der Liebling des Bassa?

PEDRILLO. Liebling, Spion und Ausbund aller Spitzbuben, der mich mit den Augen vergiften möchte, wenn's möglich wäre.

BELMONTE. O guter Pedrillo, was sagst du?

Fourth Scene

Pedrillo (alone). Afterwards Belmonte.

PEDRILLO: Go ahead, you old watchdog. We'll see who has the last laugh. And to lay a trap for you, you suspicious, hateful enemy of man, would be a real treat for me.

BELMONTE: Pedrillo, good Pedrillo!

PEDRILLO: Ah, dearest master! Is it possible? Is it really you? I had already lost all hope that any of my letters reached you.

BELMONTE: Tell me, Pedrillo, is my Constanza still alive?

PEDRILLO: She is, and devoted to you alone. Since the horrible day when our ship was captured by pirates, we have suffered many hardships. Fortunately, Pasha Selim bought all three of us. Your Constanza, I mean, my Blonda, and myself. Donna Constanza is his chosen beloved.

BELMONTE: Ah, what are you saying?

PEDRILLO: Now, now not so impetuous! As far as I know, he still is playing the unrequited lover.

BELMONTE: Are you certain? Constanza has remained faithful to me?

PEDRILLO. Nur nicht gleich verzagt! Unter uns gesagt: ich hab auch einen Stein im Brett beim Bassa. Durch mein bißchen Geschick in der Gärtnerei hab ich seine Gunst weggekriegt, und dadurch hab ich so ziemlich Freiheit, die tausend andere nicht haben würden. Da sonst jede Mannsperson sich entfernen muß, wenn eine seiner Weiber in den Garten kommt, kann ich bleiben; sie reden sogar mit mir, und er sagt nichts darüber. Freilich mault der alte Osmin, besonders, wenn mein Blondchen ihrer Gebieterin folgen muß.

BELMONTE. Ist's möglich? Du hast sie gesprochen? O sag, sag! Liebt sie mich noch?

PEDRILLO. Hm! Daß Sie daran zweifeln! Ich dächte, Sie kennten die gute Konstanze mehr als zu gut, hätten Proben genug ihrer Liebe. Doch damit dürfen wir uns gar nicht aufhalten. Hier ist bloß die Frage, wie's anzufangen ist, hier wegzukommen?

BELMONTE. O da hab ich für alles gesorgt! Ich hab hier ein Schiff in einiger Entfernung vom Hafen, das uns auf den ersten Wink einnimmt, und –

PEDRILLO. Ah, sachte, sachte! Erst müssen wir die Mädels haben, ehe wir zu Schiffe gehen, und das geht nicht so husch, husch, wie Sie meinen!

BELMONTE. O lieber, guter Pedrillo, mach nur, daß ich sie sehen, daß ich sie sprechen kann! Das Herz schlägt mir vor Angst und Freude!

PEDRILLO. Pfiffig müssen wir das Ding anfangen, und rasch müssen wir's ausführen, damit wir den alten Aufpasser übertölpeln. Bleiben Sie hier in der Nähe. Jetzt wird der Bassa bald von einer Lustfahrt auf dem Wasser zurückkommen. Ich will Sie ihm als einen geschickten Baumeister vorstellen, denn Bauen und Gärtnerei sind seine Steckenpferde. Aber lieber, goldner Herr, halten Sie sich in Schranken; Konstanze ist bei ihm –

BELMONTE. Konstanze bei ihm? Was sagst du? Ich soll sie sehen?

PEDRILLO. Gemach, gemach ums Himmels willen, lieber Herr, sonst stolpern wir! Ah, ich glaube, dort seh ich sie schon angefahren kommen. Gehn Sie nur auf die Seite, wenn er kommt; ich will ihm entgegen gehen. (Geht ab.)

PEDRILLO: Surely, dear master; but how things stand with my Blonda, Heaven only knows! The poor thing is pining away with an ugly old fellow to whom the Pasha gave her, and perhaps—I do not dare to think about it!

BELMONTE: Not the old fellow who just went into the palace?

PEDRILLO: The same. But all is not lost yet. Through my slight skill in gardening, I won the favor of the Pasha and therefore I have a good deal of freedom. But we must not lose any time. The question is: how shall we manage to get away from here?

BELMONTE: Oh, I have taken care of everything. Some distance from the harbor, I have a ship awaiting us—which will take us aboard at our first signal, and—

PEDRILLO: How, easy, easy! First we must abduct the ladies before we set sail. All that does not go in a flash, as you think.

BELMONTE: Oh dear, good Pedrillo, just arrange for me to see her, that I may speak to her! My heart is beating with anxiety and joy!

PEDRILLO: We must set to work craftily and act quickly, so that we can outwit the old watch-dog. The Pasha will return any minute from a pleasure trip on the water. But dearest, kindest master, keep yourself well in hand; Constanza is with him—

BELMONTE: (impulsively) Constanza with him?

PEDRILLO: Patience, patience, dear master, or we shall come to grief. Wait here, while I go to meet him. (he exits)

Fifth Scene

No. 4- ARIA

Schmerz, lohnt der Tren - nung ban - gen Schmerz.
part, will a - tone for days a - part.
Schon zittr' ich und wan - ke, schon zag' ich und schwanke, schon zag' ich und
I'm hop-ing and long-ing, im-pa-tient, ex-cit-ed so see us u-
schwan - ke, es hebt sich die schwel - len - de Brust. es
nit - ed. The end of my suf-f'ring is near The
hebt sich die schwel - len - de Brust, es hebt sich die schwel - len - de Brust.
end of my suf-fring is near, the end of my suf - fring is near.
Ist das ihr
Is that her
fp
pp
cresc.
f

B.
Lis - peln? Es wird mir so ban - ge.
whis - per? My an-guish is grow - ing.
p
War das ihr Seuf-zen? Es glüht mir die Wan - ge. Täuscht mich die
Was that her sigh-ing? My spir-it is glow - ing. Does love de-
Lie - be, war es ein Traum? täuscht mich die Lie - be, war es ein
ceive me. was it a dream, does love de-ceive me, was it a
Traum? täuscht mich die Lie - be, war es ein Traum? O wie ängstlich,
dream, does love de-ceive me, was it a dream? O how an-xious,
fp
p
p
o wie feu-rig klopft mein lie - be - vol - les Herz, klopft mein
O how fer-vid beats my ev - er - lov - ing heart, beats my
f
pp

B.
lie-be-vol-les Herz, klopft mein lie- - be - vol - - - - - - - -
ev-er-lov-ing heart, beats my ev - er - lov - - - - - - - -
- - - les Herz!
- - - ing heart!
pp
Ist das ihr
Is that her
Lis - peln?
whis - per?
War das ihr Seuf-zen? Es wird mir so
Was that her sighing? My an-guish is
fp
ban-ge, es glüht mir die Wan-ge, es glüht mir die Wan-ge! O wie ängst-lich, o wie
grow-ing, my spir- it is glowing, my spir-it is glowing. O how an-xious, o how
feu-rig klopft mein lie-be-vol-les Herz, klopft mein lie-be-vol-les Herz,
fervid beats my ev-er-lov-ing heart, beats my ev-er-lov-ing heart,

PEDRILLO: (Kommt hurtig gelaufen.) Geschwind, geschwind auf die Seite und versteckt! Der Bassa kommt. (Belmonte versteckt sich.)

PEDRILLO: (enters hurriedly) Hurry, hurry, hide over there! The Pasha is coming! (Belmonte hides)

Sechster Auftritt

Selim. Konstanze. Janitscharen.

(Der Bassa Selim und Konstanze kommen in einem Lustschiffe angefahren, vor welchem ein anderes Schiff mit Janitscharen voraus landet. Die Janitscharen stellen sich am Ufer in Ordnung, stimmen folgenden Chor an.)

Sixth Scene

Selim. Constanza. Janissaries.

(The Pasha Selim and Constanza arrive in a pleasure boat, preceded by another boat with Janissaries. The Janissaries line up at the shore, and sing the following chorus.)

No. 5 - CHORUS

klang.
throngs.
Tenor Solo.
klang.
throngs.
Weht ihm ent-ge - gen,
Blow gentle breez - es,
throngs.
Sopran Solo.
Eb-ne dich sanf - ter, sanf - - ter, wal-len-de Fluth.
Flow welling tor - rent, calm - ly, peacefully on.
Alt Solo.
Eb-ne dich sanf - ter, wal-len-de Fluth.
Flow welling tor - rent, peacefully on.
küh-len-de Win - de, eb - ne dich sanf - - ter, wal-len-de Fluth.
blow sweet and soft - ly, flow welling tor - rent, peacefully on.
Alt Solo.
Singt ihm der Lie - be Freu - - - den in's Herz.
Sing lov-ing praises, sing to his heart.
Tenor Solo.
Singt ihm der Lie - be Freu-den in's Herz.
Sing loving prais - es un - to his heart.
Bass Solo.
Singt ihm ent-ge - gen, flie-gen-de Chö - re, singt ihm der Lie - be Freu-den in's Herz.
Hail him ye voi - ces, great him with fer - vour, sing loving prais - es un - to his heart.

Sopran Solo.
Weht ihm ent - ge - - gen, küh - - len - de Win - -
Alt Solo.
Blow gen- tle breez - es, blow sweet and soft- -
Tenor Solo.
Singt ihm ent - ge - - gen, flie - - gen - de Chö - -
Bass Solo.
Hail him ye voic - es, greet him with fer - -
p
de; eb - ne dich sanf - - - - - - - ter, wal - len-de
ly, Flow well-ing tor - rent, peace-ful-ly
re, singt ihm der Lie - - be, der Lie - - - be Freu - den in's
vor, Hail him ye voic - es, ye voic - es sing to his
Tutti.
Fluth. Singt dem gro - ssen Bas - sa Lie - der, dem gro-ssen Bas-sa
on. Sing to might- y Pa -sha prais-es to mighty Pa-sha
Herz. Singt dem gro - ssen Bas - sa Lie - der, dem gro-ssen Bas-sa
heart. Sing, to might- y Pa -sha prais-es to mighty Pa-sha
f

Lie - der, tö - - ne, feu - ri - ger Ge - sang. und vom U - fer
praises, sing him ju - bi - lating songs. Far a - loft the
Lie - der, tö - - ne, feu - ri - ger Ge - sang, und vom U - fer
praises, sing him ju - bi - lating songs. Far a - loft the
hal - le wie - der, vom U - fer hal - le wie - der uns - rer Lie - der Ju - bel - klang, uns - rer
joy-ous
e - cho rais - es, a - loft the echo rais - es joy - ous hymns from cheer - ing throngs,
hal - le wie - der, vom U - fer hal - le wie - der uns - rer Lie - der Ju - bel - klang,
e - cho rais - es, a - loft the echo rais - es joy - ous hymns from cheer - ing throngs,
Lie - - der Ju - bel - klang, uns - rer Lie - der Ju - bel - klang.
hymns from
uns - rer Lie - der cheering throngs, joyous hymns from cheering throngs.
joyous hymns from
uns - rer Lie - der Ju - bel - klang, uns - rer Lie - der Ju - bel - klang.
joyous hymns from cheering throngs, joyous hymns from cheer ing throngs.
(Janitscharen ab)
Janissaries exeunt.

Siebenter Auftritt

Selim. Konstanze.

SELIM: Immer noch traurig, geliebte Konstanze? Immer in Tränen? Sieh, dieser schöne Abend, diese reizende Gegend, diese bezaubernde Musik, meine zärtliche Liebe für dich. Sag, kann nichts von allem dich endlich beruhigen, endlich dein Herz rühren? Sieh, ich könnte befehlen, könnte grausam mit dir verfahren, dich zwingen. (Konstanze seufzt.) Aber nein, Konstanze, dir selbst will ich dein Herz zu danken haben, dir selbst!

KONSTANZE: Grossmütiger Mann! O dass ich es könnte, dass ich's erwidern könnte — aber —

SELIM: Sag, Konstanze, sag, was hält dich zurück?

KONSTANZE: Du wirst mich hassen.

SELIM: Nein, ich schwöre dir's. Du weisst, wie sehr ich dich liebe, wieviel Freiheit ich dir vor allen meinen Weibern gestatte, dich wie meine einzige schätze.

KONSTANZE: O so verzeih!

Seventh Scene

Selim. Constanza.

PASHA SELIM: Still sad, beloved Constanza? Always in tears? Can nothing touch your heart? See—I could command, I could force my will upon you. (Constanza sighs)

But no, Constanza, you must give me your heart of your own free will.

CONSTANZA: Forgive me, Pasha, but do not ask me for a heart which is promised forever.

C.
Freu - de! Tren - - nung war mein ban - - ges Loos, und nun
fleet-ing! Now my fate is hard. to bear and my
schwimmt mein Aug' in Thränen, mein Aug! schwimmt in Thrä - nen, es schwimmt in
eyes are dim with weep-ing, my eyes are dim with weep- ing, are dim with
Thrä - nen! Kum-mer
weep-ing. I am
cresc.
sfp
ruht in mei - nem Schoos,
ruled by dark des-pair.
p
sfp
Kum-mer ruht in mei-nem Schoos, in mei - - - -
I am ruled by dark des- pair, by dark
p

C.
nem Schoos, Kummer ruht in mei-nem
des - pair, I am ruled by dark des-
Schoos, Kum-mer ruht in mei
pair. I - am ruled by dark
nem Schoos.
des - pair.
cresc.
Ach ich
Ah, in
lieb-te, war so glücklich, kann-te nicht der
lov-ing I was hap-py; sor - row's name I

Lie - - be Schmerz, kann - te nicht der Lie - be Schmerz, war so
did not know, sor - row's name I did not know, I was
cresc.
mf
p
glück-lich, kann-te nicht der Lie-be Schmerz, schwur ihm Treu-e, dem Ge-
hap-py, sor-row's name I did not know. On my lover, true and
cresc.
mf
p
lieb-ten, gab da-hin mein gan-zes Herz, gab da - hin mein gan- - zes
faith-ful, all my heart did I be - stow, all my heart, my heart be-
cresc.
sf
Herz. Doch wie schnell schwand mei-ne Freude, doch wie schnell schwand mei-ne
stow. But the hap-py days were fleeting, but the hap-py days were
p
f
p
f
p
Freu-de, Tren - nung war mein ban - ges Loos, und mein
fleet-ing! Now my fate is hard to bear, and my

C.
Au - ge schwimmt in Thrä - nen, mein Au - ge schwimmt in Thränen, es schwimmt in
eyes are dim with weep - ing, my eyes are dim with weeping, are dim with
sfp
sfp
sfp
Thrä - nen;
weep-ing;
cresc.
sfp
sfp
sfp
sfp
Kummer
I am
ruht in mei - nem Schoos,
ruled by dark despair.
p
sfp
sfp
sfp
Kum-mer ruht in mei - nem Schoos, in mei -
I am ruled by dark des-pair, by dark

C.
cresc.
nem
des-
Schoos,
pair.
Kum - mer
I am
ruht in
ruled.
mei - nem
by dark des- pair,
Schoos,
Kum - mer
I am
sf
p
ruht in mei - nem Schoos, in mei - nem Schoos, in mei - nem
ruled by dark des pair, by dark des - pair, by dark des
cresc.
Schoos.
pair.
f

KONSTANZE. Ach, ich sagt es wohl, du würdest mich hassen. Aber verzeih, verzeih dem liebekranken Mädchen! Du bist ja so großmütig, so gut. Ich will dir dienen, deine Sklavin sein bis ans Ende meines Lebens, nur verlange nicht ein Herz von mir, das auf ewig versagt ist.

SELIM. Ha, Undankbare! Was wagst du zu bitten?

KONSTANZE. Töte mich, Selim, töte mich, nur zwinge mich nicht, meineidig zu werden! Noch zuletzt, wie mich der Seeräuber aus den Armen meines Geliebten riß, schwur ich aufs feierlichste-

SELIM. Halt ein, nicht ein Wort! Reize meinen Zorn nicht noch mehr. Bedenke, daß du in meiner Gewalt bist!

KONSTANZE. Ich bin es, aber du wirst dich ihrer nicht bedienen, ich kenne dein gutes, dein mitleidsvolles Herz. Hätte ich's sonst wagen können, dir das meinige zu entdecken?

SELIM. Wag es nicht, meine Güte zu mißbrauchen!

KONSTANZE. Nur Aufschub gönne mir, Herr, nur Zeit, meinen Schmerz zu vergessen!

SELIM. Wie oft schon gewährt ich dir diese Bitte.

KONSTANZE. Nur noch diesmal!

SELIM. Es sei, zum letzten Male! Geh, Konstanze, geh! Besinne dich eines Bessern, und morgen—

KONSTANZE (im Abgehn). Unglückliches Mädchen! O Belmonte, Belmonte!

Achter Auftritt

Selim. Pedrillo. Belmonte.

SELIM. Ihr Schmerz, ihre Tränen, ihre Standhaftigkeit bezaubern mein Herz immer mehr, machen mir ihre Liebe nur noch wünschenswerter. Ha, wer wollte gegen ein solches Herz Gewalt brauchen? Nein, Konstanze, nein, auch Selim hat ein Herz, auch Selim kennt Liebe!

PEDRILLO. Herr, verzeih, daß ich es wage, dich in deinen Betrachtungen zu stören!

SELIM. Was willst du, Pedrillo?

PEDRILLO. Dieser junge Mann, der sich in Italien mit vielem Fleiß auf die Baukunst gelegt, hat von deiner Macht, von deinem Reichtum gehört und kommt her, dir als Baumeister seine Dienste anzubieten.

BELMONTE. Herr, könnte ich so glücklich sein, durch meine geringen Fähigkeiten deinen Beifall zu verdienen!

SELIM. Hm! Du gefällst mir. Ich will sehen, was du kannst. (Zu Pedrillo.) Sorge für seinen Unterhalt. Morgen werde ich dich wieder rufen lassen. (Geht ab.)

Eighth Scene

Selim. Pedrillo. Belmonte.

SELIM: Her tears, her fortitude enchant my heart more and more and make her love only more desirable to me. Who would ever use force against such a heart?

PEDRILLO: (entering with Belmonte) Great Pasha, forgive me for disturbing your meditations.

SELIM: What do you wish, Pedrillo?

PEDRILLO: (indicating Belmonte) This young man who has been very diligently practicing his profession of architecture in Italy, has heard of your power and your wealth, and has come to offer you his services.

BELMONTE: Sire, if only I could be so fortunate as to win your approval through my modest talents!

SELIM: You please me. I should like to see what you can do.
(to Pedrillo) Take good care of him. Tomorrow I shall have you called again. (he leaves)

Neunter Auftritt

Belmonte. Pedrillo.

PEDRILLO. Ha! Triumph, Triumph, Herr! Der erste Schritt war getan.

BELMONTE. Ach, laß mich zu mir sebst kommen! Ich habe sie gesehen, hab das gute, treue, beste Mädchen gesehen! O Konstanze, Konstanze! Was könnt ich für dich tun, was für dich wagen?

PEDRILLO. Ha! Gemach, gemach, bester Herr! Stimmen Sie den Ton ein bißchen herab; Verstellung wird uns weit bessere Dienste leisten. Wir sind nicht in unserm Vaterlande. Hier fragen sie den Henker darnach, ob's einen Kopf mehr oder weniger in der Welt gibt. Bastonade und Strick um Hals sind hier wie ein Morgenbrot.

BELMONTE. Ach, Pedrillo, wenn du die Liebe kenntest!

PEDRILLO. Hm! Als wenn's mit unser einem gar nichts wäre. Ich habe so gut meine zärtlichen Stunden als andere Leute. Und denken Sie denn, daß mir's nicht auch im Bauche grimmt, wenn ich mein Blondchen von so einem alten Spitzbuben, wie der Osmin ist, bewacht sehen muß?

BELMONTE. O wenn es möglich wäre, sie zu sprechen –

PEDRILLO. Wir wollen sehen, was zu tun ist. Kommen Sie nur mit mir in den Garten, aber um alles in der Welt vorsichtig und fein. Denn hier ist alles Aug und Ohr. (Sie wollen in den Palast, Osmin kommt ihnen in der Tür entgegen und hält sie zurück)

Ninth Scene

Belmonte. Pedrillo.

PEDRILLO: Success! Master! The first steps have been taken. Now come with me into the garden, but, for Heaven's sake, be careful. Here the walls have ears!

Zehnter Auftritt

Osmin. Die Vorigen.

OSMIN. Wohin?

PEDRILLO. Hinein!

OSMIN (zu Belmonte). Was will das Gesicht? Zurück mit dir, zurück!

PEDRILLO. Ha, gemach, Meister Grobian, gemach! Er ist in des Bassa Diensten.

OSMIN. In des Henkers Diensten mag er sein! Er soll nicht herein!

PEDRILLO. Er soll aber herein!

OSMIN. Kommt mir nur einen Schritt über die Schwelle –

BELMONTE. Unverschämter! Hast du nicht mehr Achtung für einen Mann meines Standes?

OSMIN. Ei, Ihr mögt mir vom Stande sein! Fort, fort, oder ich will euch Beine machen.

PEDRILLO. Alter Dummkopf! Es ist ja der Baumeister, den der Bassa angenommen hat.

OSMIN. Meinethalben sei er Stockmeister, nur komm er mir nicht zu nahe. Ich müßte nicht sehen, daß es so ein Kumpan deines Gelichters ist, und daß das so eine abgeredete Karte ist, uns zu überlisten. Der Bassa ist weich wie Butter, mit dem könnt ihr machen was ihr wollt, aber ich habe eine feine Nase. Gaunerei ist's um den ganzen Kram, mit euch fremden Gesindel; und ihr abgefeimten Betrüger habt lange ein Plänchen angelegt, eure Pfiffe auszuführen; aber wart' ein bißchen! Osmin schläft nicht. Wär ich Bassa, ihr wär't längst gespießt. Ja, schneid't nur Gesichter, lacht nur höhnisch in den Bart hinein!

PEDRILLO. Ereifere dich nicht so, Alter, es hilft dir doch nichts. Sieh, soeben werden wir hinein spazieren.

OSMIN. Ha, das will ich sehen! (Stellt sich vor die Tür.)

PEDRILLO. Mach keine Umstände.

BELMONTE. Weg, Niederträchtiger!

Tenth Scene

Osmin. Pedrillo. Belmonte.

OSMIN: Whereto?

PEDRILLO: Inside.

OSMIN: What does this dog-face want? Back with you, back!

PEDRILLO: Calmly, Master Grouch! He is in the Pasha's service.

OSMIN: He may be in the hangman's service, but he's not going in.

PEDRILLO: But he is going in!

OSMIN: Don't come near me! If I were the Pasha, you would have been hanged long ago.

PEDRILLO: Don't flare up like that, old man, it won't help you. See, we are just going inside.

OSMIN: I should like to see that!

No. 7-TERZET

Allegro.
Osmin.
O.
Marsch! marsch! marsch! trollt euch fort, sonst soll die Ba-sto-
On your way! Off you go, or else the bas-ti-
f
p
Belmonte.
B.
O.
na-de euch gleich zu Dien-sten steh'n, euch gleich zu Diensten steh'n.
-na-do will make you both o-bey, will make you both o-bey.
Ei, ei,
You don't
ei,
say.
das wär' ja Scha-de, mit uns so um-zu-geh'n, mit uns so um-zu-
What a bra-va-do, to treat us in that way, to treat us in that
Pedrillo.
P.
Ei, ei, ei,
You don't say.
das wär' ja Scha-de, mit uns so um-zu-geh'n, mit
What a bra-va-do, to treat us in that way, to
geh'n.
way.
Weg von der Thü-re, weg von der
Then clear the door way, then clear the
uns so um-zu-geh'n.
treat us in that way.
Weg von der Thü-re, weg von der
Then clear the door way, then clear the
Osm.
Kommt nur nicht nä-her, kommt nur nicht nä-her,
Do not come near me, do not come near me,
f
sf

B.
Thü-re, wir geh'n hin- -ein,
door way, we will get by.
P.
Thü-re, wir geh'n hin- -ein,
door way, we will get by,
O.
sonst schlag' ich drein, sonst schlag' ich drein, sonst schlag' ich
You won't get by, you won't get by. You won't get
fp
wir geh'n hin- -ein,
we will get by,
wir geh'n hin- -ein,
we will get by,
drein, sonst schlag' ich drein, sonst schlag' ich drein, sonst schlag' ich
by, you won't get by, don't even try. don't ev-en
wir gehn hin - ein, wir gehn hin - ein, wir gehn hin - ein, wir gehn hin - ein!
we will get by, we will get by, we will get by, we will get by!
wir gehn hin - ein, wir gehn hin - ein!
we will get by, we will get by!
drein, sonst schlag' ich drein, sonst schlag' ich drein, sonst schlag' ich drein!
try, don't e-ven try, don't e- ven try, don't e - ven try!
cresc.
f

B.
Platz! fort, Platz! fort, Platz! fort! Wir geh'n hin-
Move, on! Move, on! move, on! we will get
P.
Platz! fort. Platz! fort, Platz! fort! Wir geh'n hinein, wir geh'n hin - ein.
Move, on Move, on, Move, on! We will get by, we will get by.
O.
Marsch! fort, marsch! fort, marsch! fort!
out, out out, out, out, out!
p
fp
fp fp fp fp fp fp
fp
B.
ein, wir geh'n hin - ein, ja, wir geh'n hin - ein, wir geh'n hin -
by, we will get by, yes, we will get by, we will get
P.
wir geh'n hin - ein, wir geh'n hin - ein, wir geh'n hin -
we will get by, we will get by, we will get
O.
Ich schlage drein, ich schlage drein, ich schla - ge drein, ich schla - ge
You won't get by, you won't get by, don't e-ven try, don't ev- en
fp
cresc.
B.
ein, wir geh'n hin - ein! Wir geh'n hin-ein, wir geh'n hin-ein, wir geh'n hin-
by, we will get by! We will get by, we will get by, we will get
P.
ein, wir geh'n hin - ein! Wir geh'n hin-
by, we will get by! we will get
O.
drein. ich schla - ge drein! Marsch! marsch! marsch! Trollt euch
try, don't e- ven try! On your way Off you
f
f
p

B.
ein, wir geh'n hin - ein! Ei! ei! ei! das wär' ja Schade, wär' ja Scha-de!
by, we will get by! You don't say what a bra-va-do, what bra-va- do!
P.
ein, wir geh'n hin - ein! Das wär' ja Schade! Ei! ei! ei! wir geh'n hin-
by, we will get by! What a bra-va- do! You don't say, you can not
O.
fort! Marsch! marsch! marsch! trollt euch fort! Marsch! marsch!
go. On your way, off you go. On your
f
p
f
B.
Wir geh'n hin-ein, wir geh'n hin-ein! Ei, ei, ei, ei, ei, ei, ei,
You can not treat us in this way, you can-not treat us in this
P.
ein, wir geh'n hin - ein! Ei, ei, ei, ei, ei, ei, ei,
treat us in this way! You can not treat us in this
O.
marsch! trollt euch fort! Sonst soll die Bas-to - na-de euch gleich zu Diensten
way! Off you go. or else the bas-ti-na-do will make you both o-
p
pp
B.
ei, das wär' ja Scha-de, wär' ja Scha - de, mit uns so um-zu-geh'n!
way, what a bra-va-do, what bra- va - do, to treat us in this way!
P.
ei, das wär' ja Scha-de, wär' ja Scha - de, mit uns so um-zu-geh'n!
way, what a bra-va-do, what bra- va - do, to treat us in this way!
O.
steh'n, sonst soll die Ba - sto - na - de euch gleich zu Diensten steh'n! Ich schla-ge
bey. or else the ba - sti - na - do, will make you both o- bey. You won't get.
f
fp

B.
P.
O.
Wir geh'n hin- - - - ein, wir
We will get by, we
Wir geh'n hin- - ein,
We will get by.
drein, ich schla - ge drein!
by, you won't get by!
Ich schlage drein, ich schla-ge
You won't get by, you won't get
fp
geh'n hin- - - - ein!
will get by!
wir geh'n hin- - ein, wir geh'n hin - ein, wir geh'n hin - ein, wir geh'n hin-
We will get by, we will get by, we will get by, we will get
drein!
by!
Ich schla-ge drein, ich schla-ge drein, ich schla-ge
You won't get by, you won't get by, you won't get
Wir geh'n hin - ein, wir geh'n hin - ein, wir geh'n hin - ein, wir geh'n hin-
We will get by, we will get by, we will get by, we will get
ein, wir geh'n hin - ein,
by, we will get by,
wir geh'n hin - ein, wir geh'n hin-
we will get by, we will get
drein, ich schla-ge drein, ich schla - ge drein, ich schla - ge
by, you won't get by, don't e ven try, don't e- ven
cresc.
f

Allegro assai.
B.
ein! Platz! fort, fort, fort, fort,
by! Make way for us Os-
P.
ein! Platz! fort, fort, fort, fort,
by! Make way for us Os-
O.
drein! Marsch! fort, marsch! fort, marsch! fort!
try! You nev- er will go in.
Allegro assai.
f
p
3
B.
fort! Platz! fort, fort, fort!
min! Make way! Make way!
P.
fort! Platz! fort, fort, fort, fort, fort!
min! Make way, make way, make way!
O.
Marsch! fort, fort, fort, fort, fort! Ich schlage
A- way, a- way, a- way! You won't go
cresc.
3
B.
Wir geh'n hin-ein, wir geh'n hin-ein, wir geh'n hin-ein, wir geh'n hin-
We will go in. we will go in, we will go in, we will go
P.
Wir geh'n hinein, wir geh'n hin-ein, wir geh'n hin-ein, wir geh'n hin-
We will go in, we will go in, we will go in, we will go
O.
drein, ich schlage drein, ich schla-ge drein, ich schlage drein, ich schlage
in, you won't go in, you won't go in you won't go in, you won't go
3
f

B.
ein, wir geh'n hin - ein, wir geh'n hin-ein, wir geh'n hin - ein, wir geh'n hin -
in, make way, make way, no mat-ter what you say, no mat-ter what you
P.
ein, wir geh'n hin - ein, wir geh'n hin-ein, wir geh'n hin - ein, wir geh'n hin -
in, make way, make way, no mat-ter what you say, no mat-ter what you
O.
drein, ich schla - ge drein! Marsch!
in, a - way a - way. Out
B.
ein! Platz! fort, wir geh'n hin - ein, wir geh'n hin -
say. Make way, we will go in, we will go
P.
ein! Platz! fort, wir geh'n hin - ein, wir geh'n hin -
say. Make way, we will go in, we will go
O.
fort, ich schla - ge drein, marsch! fort, ich schla - ge
out, you won't go in. Out, out, you won't go
B.
ein, wir geh'n hinein, wir geh'n hin - ein, wir geh'n hin - ein! Platz! fort, wir geh'n hin -
in, no mat-ter what you say, no mat-ter what you say! Make way, we will go
P.
ein, wir geh'n hinein, wir geh'n hin - ein, wir geh'n hin - ein! Platz! fort, wir geh'n hin -
in, no mat-ter what you say, no mat-ter what you say! Make way, we will go
O.
drein! Marsch! fort, ich schlage drein, marsch
in. out, out! You won't go in out

Ende des ersten Actes.
(End of the first act)

<table>
<tr>
<td>

ZWEITER AUFZUG

Garten am Palast des Bassa Selim; an der Seite Osmins Wohnung.

Erster Auftritt

Osmin. Blonde.

BLONDE: O des Zankens, Befehlens und Murrens wird auch kein Ende! Einmal für allemal: das steht mir nicht an! Denkst du alter Murrkopf etwa eine türkische Sklavin vor dir zu haben, die bei deinen Befehlen zittert? O da irrst du dich sehr! Mit europäischen Mädchen springt man nicht so herum; denen begegnet man ganz anders.

</td>
<td>

SECOND ACT

Garden of Pasha Selim's palace. On one side Osmin's house.

First Scene

Osmin. Blonda.

BLONDA: Oh, will there never be an end to your scolding, ordering about and grumbling? Do you think, by chance, that you have a Turkish slave before you, who trembles at your commands? European girls you don't treat in this way. You treat them in quite a different manner!

</td>
</tr>
</table>

No. 8 - ARIA

Bl.
Lieb' als Treu' ent - weicht, macht, dass in we - nig Tagen so Lieb' als Treu' ent-
love and faith de - part, will only make us stub-born, and: love and faith de-
weicht, so Lieb' als Treu' ent-weicht. Durch
part, make love and faith de-part. With
fp
Zärt-lich-keit und Schmeicheln, Ge-fäl-lig-keit und Scherzen er-o-bert man die
ten-der-ness and kind-ness, and friendliness and joking, you win without pro-
Her-zen der gu-ten Mädchen leicht, der gu-ten Mädchen leicht. Doch mür-risches Be-
vok-ing a gentle maid-en's heart, a gen-tle maid-en's heart. But sur-ly domin
cresc.
p
feh - len, und Pol - tern, Zan-ken, Pla-gen, und Pol - tern, Zan-ken, Pla-gen macht,
eer-ing, and nag-ging, shout-ing, sneer-ing, and nag-ging, shouting sneer-ing will
sf
p
sf
cresc.
f

Bl.
dass in we - nig Ta-gen so Lieb' als Treu' ent - weicht,
on-ly make us stub-born, and love and faith de - part,
p
f
p
fp
so Lieb' als Treu' ent - weicht.
and love and faith de - part.
fp
Durch Zärt-lich-keit und Schmeicheln, Ge-
With ten-der-ness and kind - ness, and
p
fäl-lig-keit und Scher - zen er - o - bert man die Her - zen der
friendliness and jok - ing you win without pro - vok - ing a
gu - ten Mäd-chen leicht.
gen - tle maid-en's heart!
f

OSMIN. Ei seht doch mal, was das Mädchen vorschreiben kann! Zärtlichkeit? Schmeicheln? Es ist mir wie pure Zärtlichkeit! Wer Teufel hat dir das Zeug in den Kopf gesetzt? Hier sind wir in der Türkei, und da geht's aus einem andern Tone. Ich dein Herr, du meine Sklavin; ich befehle, du mußt gehorchen!

BLONDE. Deine Sklavin? Ich deine Sklavin? Ha, ein Mädchen eine Sklavin! Noch einmal sag mir das, noch einmal!

OSMIN (für sich). Ich möchte toll werden, was das Mädchen für ein starrköpfiges Ding ist. (Laut.) Du hast doch wohl nicht vergessen, daß dich der Bassa mir zur Sklavin geschenkt hat?

BLONDE. Bassa hin, Bassa her! Mädchen sind keine Ware zum verschenken! Ich bin eine Engländerin, zur Freiheit geboren und trotz jedem, der mich zu etwas zwingen will!

OSMIN (beiseite). Gift und Dolch über das Mädchen! Beim Mahomet, sie macht mich rasend. Und doch lieb ich die Spitzbübin, trotz ihres tollen Kopfes! (Laut.) Ich befehle dir, augenblicklich mich zu lieben!

BLONDE. Hahaha! Komm mir nur ein wenig näher, ich will dir fühlbare Beweise davon geben.

OSMIN. Tolles Ding! Weißt du, daß du mein bist und ich dich dafür züchtigen kann?

BLONDE. Wag's nicht, mich anzurühren, wenn dir deine Augen lieb sind.

OSMIN. Wie? Du unterstehst dich—

BLONDE. Da ist was zu unterstehen! Du bist der Unverschämte, der sich zuviel Freiheit herausnimmt. So ein altes häßliches Gesicht untersteht sich, einem Mädchen wie ich, jung, schön, zur Freude geboren, wie einer Magd zu befehlen! Wahrhaftig, das stünde mir an! Uns gehört das Regiment; ihr seid unsere Sklaven und glücklich, wenn ihr Verstand genug habt, euch die Ketten zu erleichtern.

OSMIN. Bei meinem Bart, sie ist toll! Hier, hier in der Türkei?

BLONDE. Türkei hin, Türkei her! Weib ist Weib, sie sei wo sie wolle! Sind eure Weiber solche Närrinnen, sich von euch unterjochen zu lassen, desto schlimmer für sie; in Europa verstehen sie das Ding besser. Laß mich nur einmal Fuß hier gefaßt haben, sie sollen bald anders werden.

OSMIN. Beim Allah, die wär imstande, uns allen die Weiber rebellisch zu machen! Aber—

BLONDE. Aufs Bitten müßt ihr euch legen, wenn ihr etwas von uns erhalten wollt; besonders Liebhaber deines Gelichters.

OSMIN. Freilich, wenn ich Pedrillo wär, so ein Drahtpüppchen wie er, da wär ich vermutlich willkommen, denn euer Mienenspiel hab ich lange weg.

BLONDE. Erraten, guter Alter, erraten! Das kannst du dir wohl einbilden, daß mir der niedliche Pedrillo lieber ist, wie dein Blasebalggesicht. Also wenn du klug wärst—

OSMIN. Sollt ich dir die Freiheit geben, zu tun und zu machen, was du wolltest, he?

BLONDE. Besser würdest du immer dabei fahren: denn so wirst du sicher betrogen.

OSMIN. Gift und Dolch! Nun reißt mir die Geduld! Den Augenblick hinein ins Haus! Und wo du's wagst—

BLONDE. Mach mich nicht lachen.

OSMIN. Ins Haus, sag ich!

BLONDE. Nicht von der Stelle!

OSMIN. Mach nicht, daß ich Gewalt brauche.

OSMIN: Oho! Just listen to what the little lady prescribes! Tenderness? Caresses? Who the devil put such rubbish into your head? Here we are in Turkey, and the music is in a different key. I am your master, you are my slave. I command, you obey.

BLONDA: I, your slave? Tell me that once more!

OSMIN: By Mohammed, she drives me wild! But I love the little rascal in spite of her crazy notions. (aside)

(aloud) I command you to fall in love with me this very moment.

BLONDA: Ha ha ha! Come just a bit nearer to me and I shall give you feeling proof of my love.

OSMIN: By allah, she is capable of making all our women rebellious. But—

BLONDA: You must come crawling on your hands and knees, if you wish to obtain something from us, especially lovers of your ilk.

OSMIN: To be sure, if I were Pedrillo, such a young pup as he, it would be more agreeable to you!

BLONDA: You guessed it, my good old fellow! My handsome Pedrillo is dearer to me than you and your bellows-face- So—if you had sense—

OSMIN: Poison and daggers! Now I have lost patience. Into the house, this minute! And if you dare—

BLONDA: You make me laugh!

OSMIN: Into the house, I say!

BLONDA: I won't move from the spot!

OSMIN: Don't make me use force!

BLONDE. Gewalt werd ich mit Gewalt vertreiben. Meine Gebieterin hat mich hier in den Garten bestellt; sie ist die Geliebte des Bassa, sein Augapfel, sein alles; und es kostet mich ein Wort, so hast du fünfzig auf die Fußsohlen. Also geh!

OSMIN (für sich). Das ist ein Satan! Ich muß nachgeben, so wahr ich ein Muselmann bin; sonst könnte ihre Drohung eintreffen.

BLONDA: Then I shall meet force with force. My mistress is the Pasha's beloved, and it costs me but a word to have you get 50 lashes on the soles of your feet.

OSMIN: (to himself) That is a she-devil!

No. 9- DUET

Bl.
fällt dir da ein! Fort, lass mich al - lein!
leave me a-lone! Go, leave me a - lone!
O.
zum Hen - ker! Beim Al-lah! ich wer-de nicht
O hang it! By Al-lah, I'll stay here for-
f
p
O.
gehen, ich wer-de nicht gehen, ich wer-de nicht gehen, bis du
ev-er, I'll stay here for-ev-er I'll stay here for-ev-er till you
f
p
O.
zu ge-hor - chen mir schwörst, bis du zu ge-hor-chen mir
swear to do what I say, till you swear to do what I
fp
Blonde.
Bl.
Nicht so viel, nicht so viel, nicht so viel, nicht
I'll nev-er, I'll nev-er, I'll nev-er, I'll
O.
schwörst, zu ge-hor - chen mir schwörst.
say, — swear to do what I say.
fp
f p
f p
f p
Bl.
so viel, nicht so viel, nicht so viel, nicht so viel, das sollst du bald sehen,
nev-er, I'll nev-er not this time or ev - er, not this time or ev-er.
f p
fp
fp
cresc.
f

Bl.
und wenn du der Gross-mo-gul wärst,
Not if you were the Pa-sha him-self.
p
und wenn du der Gross-mo-gul wärst, wenn du der Gross-, der Gross-mo-gul wärst.
if you were the Pa-sha him-self, not if you were the Pa-sha himself.
fp
f
Andante. Osm.
O.
O Eng-län-der! seid ihr nicht Tho-ren, ihr lasst eu-ern Wei-bern den
O Eng-lish-men, you are mis-guid-ed, how can you give in to your
Blonde.
Ein Mädchen zur Frei-heit ge-bo-ren, lässt nie sich als Scla-vin be-
A woman ac-cust-omed to free-dom, will ne-ver sur-ren-der to
Wil-len!
wom-en!
feh-len; und ist auch die Freiheit ver-lo-ren, doch bleibt sie noch
slav'-ry and fight-ing with cour-age and brav'-ry, will not give in
Wie ist man ge-plagt und ge-scho-ren, wenn man so ein Früchtchen, ein
Mis-treat-ed I am and de-rid-ed a hus-sy like this one is

Bl.
O.
Für-stin der Welt. Ein Mädchen zur Frei-heit ge - bo - ren, lässt nie sich als Scla-vin be -
till she is free. A wom-an ac-cust-omed to free- -dom, will never sur-ren-der to
Früchtchen er-hält! O Eng-län-der! O Engländer! O Eng-län-der! seid ihr nicht
too much for me! O Eng-lish-men! O Englishmen! O Englishmen, you are mis-
feh-len, und ist auch die Frei-heit ver - lo - - ren. doch bleibt sie noch
slav-ry and fight-ing with cour-age and brav'-ry, will not give in
Tho-ren! Wie ist man ge-plagt und ge - scho - ren, wenn man so ein Früchtchen, ein
guided- mis-treat-ed I am and de- rid - ed a hus-sy like this one is
mfp
Für - stin der Welt, und ist auch die Frei - heit ver - lo - - ren,
til she is free and fight-ing with cour-age and brav' 'ry
Frücht-chen er - hält! wie ist man ge - plagt und ge - - scho - - ren, wenn
too much for me, mis-treat-ed I am and de - ri - ded. A
doch bleibt sie noch Für-stin der Welt. doch bleibt sie noch Für-stin der Welt
will not give in til she is free. Will not give in til she is free-
man so ein Früchtchen, ein Früchtchen er - hält. wenn man so ein Früchtchen, ein Früchtchen erhält!
hus-sy like this one is too much for me, a hus-sy like this one is too much for me.
pp

Allegro assai.
Bl.
Nun troll' dich,
Be off now,
nun troll' dich!
be off now!
O.
So sprichst du mit mir?
You send me a-way?
So
You
Allegro assai.
f
p
f
p
Bl.
Nicht anders,
Pre-cisely,
nicht anders!
pre-cisely!
O.
sprichst du mit mir?
send me a-way?
Nun bleib' ich erst hier,
The long-er I'll stay
nun bleib' ich erst hier, nun bleib' ich erst
the long-er I'll stay, the long-er I'll
fp
fp
fp
fp
p
f
(Stösst ihn fort.) (Pushes him away)
Bl.
Ein andermal, jetzt musst du gehen,
Some other time, in-solent brag-ger,
ein andermal, jetzt musst du
some other time, insolent
O.
hier, nun bleib' ich erst hier.
stay, the long-er I'll stay.
Wer hat solche Frechheit ge-sehen,
Was ev-er so bra-zen a swag-ger,
wer
was
p
f
p
f
p
f
p
f
Bl.
gehen,
brag-ger.
ein andermal, jetzt musst du gehen,
Some other time, in-so-lent brag-ger,
ein andermal, jetzt musst du
some other time, in-so-lent
O.
hat solche Frechheit ge-sehen,
ev-er so bra-zen a swag-ger,
wer hat solche Frechheit ge-se-hen,
was ev-er so bra-zen a swag-ger,
wer
was
p
f
p
f
p

(pretends to scratch out his eyes)
(stellt sich, als wolle sie ihm die Augen auskratzen.)
Bl.
ge - hen, jetzt musst du ge - hen: es ist um die Au-gen ge-
brag-ger, boist- er- ous brag-ger! You better get out in a
O.
hat sol-che Frech- - heit ge- se - hen!
ev - er so braz - en a swag-ger!
cresc.
f
p
schehen, es ist um die Au-gen ge-schehen, wo- - fern du noch län - ger ver-
hurry, you better get out in a hurry- or else I will kick and I'll
Nur
Be
weilst. (timidly drawing back)
bite. (furchtsam zurückweichend.)
ru-hig, ich will ja gern ge-hen, nur ru-hig, ich will ja gern ge-hen,
si-lent, I leave you, don't worry, be si-lent, I leave you, don't worry.
Nun troll' dich. nicht
Be off now! Pre-
be- - - vor du gar Schlä - ge er-theilst. So sprichst du mit
I'm not in the mood for a fight. You send me a-

Bl.
an-ders. Ein an-der-mal, jetzt musst du ge-hen, es
cisely! Some other time, in- so- lent bragger. You
O.
mir? Nun bleib' ich erst hier. Wer hat sol-che Frech-heit ge-
way, The long-er I'll stay. Was ev-er so braz-en a
p
Bl.
ist um die Au-gen ge-sche-hen, wo-fern du noch län-ger ver-
bet-ter get out in a hurry. or else I will kick and I'll
O.
se-hen? Nur ru-hig, ich will ja gern ge-hen, be-
swag-ger? Be si-lent, I leave you, don't worry I'm
Bl.
weilst; es ist um die Au-gen ge-schehen,
bite You bet-ter get out in a hur-ry.
O.
vor du gar Schläge er-theilst. Nur ru-hig, ich will ja gern
not in the mood for a fight! Be si-lent, I leave you, don't
Bl.
wo- - - -fern du noch län-ger ver-weilst; es
or else I will kick and I'll bite, you
O.
ge-hen, be- - - -vor du gar Schlä-ge er-theilst.
wor-ry I'm not in the mood for a fight.
f

Zweiter Auftritt

Blonde. Konstanze.

BLONDE: Wie traurig das gute Mädchen daher kommt! Freilich tut's weh, den Geliebten zu verlieren und Sklavin zu sein. Es geht mir wohl auch nicht viel besser; aber ich habe doch noch das Vergnügen, meinen Pedrillo manchmal zu sehen, ob's gleich auch mager und verstohlen genug geschehen muss; doch wer kann wider den Strom schwimmen!

Second Scene

No. 10 - RECITATIVE AND ARIA

C.
Leiden,
sadness,
banger Sehnsucht Leiden
hopeless yearning's sadness
woh - nen nun da-
now has come to
für in der beklemmten Brust.
dwell within my anguished heart.
Andante con moto.
Trau - rig - keit
Mournful grief
ward mir zum Loo-se, ward mir zum Loo-se, weil ich dir ent-ris-sen bin,
ill-fate im - pos-es, ill-fate im - pos-es; from your arms have I been torn,
weil ich dir ent-ris - sen bin. weil ich dir,
from your arms have I been torn, from your arms,
weil ich dir ent - ris - sen bin. Gleich der wurmzer-nag-ten Ro - se,
from your arms have I been torn. Like the wast-ed blighted ros- es,
p
sf
f
mf

gleich dem Gras im Win-ter-moo-se welkt mein ban-ges Le-ben hin. mein
like the win-ter's ash-en moss-es fades my life in days for-lorn, my
ban-ges Le-ben hin.
life in days for-lorn.
Selbst der Luft darf ich nicht
when I tell the gen-tle
sa-gen
breez-es
mei-ner See-le bit-tern Schmerz, mei-ner
of my spir-it's bit-ter smart, of my
See-le bit-tern Schmerz. Denn un-wil-lig, ihn zu tragen, haucht sie
spir-it's bit-ter smart, then un-feel-ing un-re-lent-ing, they re-
al-le mei-ne Kla-gen wie-der in mein ar-mes
turn all my la-ment-ing to my tor-tured, broken
p
sf
sfp
cresc.

Herz, wie- - -der in mein ar- - -mes Herz, wie-der
heart, to my tor - tured bro - ken heart, to my

in mein ar-mes Herz. wie-der in mein ar-mes Herz. Trau - rig-keit,
tor-tured bro-ken heart, to my tor-tured bro-ken heart. Mourn- ful grief,

Trau - rig - keit, Trau - rig - keit
mourn - ful grief, mourn- ful grief,

ward mir zum Loo-se, ward mir zum Loo-se, weil ich dir ent-ris-sen bin,
ill-fate im-pos-es, ill-fate im-pos-es; from your arms have I been torn,

weil ich dir ent-ris-sen bin. weil ich dir,
from your arms have I oeen torn, from your arms,

C.
weil ich dir entrissen bin. Gleich der
from your arms have I been torn, Like the
p
wurm-zer-nag-ten Ro-se, gleich dem Gras im Win-ter-moo-se welkt mein
wast-ed, blight-ed ros-es, like the win-ter's ash-en moss-es fades my
cresc.
ban-ges Le-ben hin, mein ban-ges
life in days for-lorn, my life in
Le-ben hin. Selbst der
days for-lorn. When I
cresc.
Luft darf ich nicht sa-gen mei-ner See-le bit-tern
tell the gen-tle breez-es of my spirit's bit-ter

Schmerz, mei - ner See - le bit - tern Schmerz, denn un - wil - lig ihn zu
smart, of my spir - it's bit - ter smart, then un - feel - ing, un - re -
sf p sf p
sfp sfp
tragen, haucht sie al - le mei - ne Kla - - - gen
lent - ing they re - turn all my la - ment - - - ing
cresc.
f
wie - der in mein ar - mes Herz, wie - der in mein ar - mes Herz, wie - der
to my tor - tured broken heart, to my tor - tured bro - ken heart, to my
p sf sfp
in mein ar - mes Herz, wie - der in mein ar - - -
tor - tured bro - ken heart, to my tor - tured, tor - - -
sf p sf p
- mes, ar - mes Herz.
- tured bro - ken heart.
tr

BLONDE. Ach mein bestes Fräulein, noch immer so traurig?

KONSTANZE. Kannst du fragen, die du meinen Kummer weißt? Wieder ein Abend, und noch keine Nachricht, noch keine Hoffnung! Und morgen– ach Gott, ich darf nicht daran denken!

BLONDE. Heitern Sie sich wenigstens ein bißchen auf. Sehn Sie, wie schön der Abend ist, wie blühend uns alles entgegenlacht, wie freudig uns die Vögel zu ihrem Gesang einladen! Verbannen Sie die Grillen, und fassen Sie Mut!

KONSTANZE. Wie glücklich bist du, Mädchen, bei deinem Schicksal so gelassen zu sein! O daß ich es auch könnte!

BLONDE. Das steht nur bei Ihnen, hoffen Sie–

KONSTANZE. Wo nicht der mindeste Schein von Hoffnung mehr zu erblicken ist?

BLONDE. Hören Sie nur: ich verzage mein Lebtag nicht, es mag auch eine Sache noch so schlimm aussehen. Denn wer sich immer das Schlimmste vorstellt, ist auch wahrhaftig am schlimmsten dran.

KONSTANZE. Und wer sich immer mit Hoffnung schmeichelt und zuletzt betrogen sieht, hat alsdann nichts mehr übrig als die Verzweiflung.

BLONDE. Jedes nach seiner Weise. Ich glaube bei der meinigen am besten zu fahren. Wie bald kann Ihr Belmonte mit Lösegeld erscheinen oder uns listiger Weise entführen? Wären wir die ersten Frauenzimmer, die den türkischen Vielfraßen entkämen? Dort seh ich den Bassa.

KONSTANZE. Laß uns ihm aus den Augen gehn.

BLONDE. Zu spät. Er hat Sie schon gesehen. Ich darf aber getrost aus dem Wege trollen, er schaffte mich ohnehin fort. (Im Weggehen.) Courage, wir kommen gewiß noch in unsre Heimat!

Dritter Auftritt

Konstanze. Selim.

SELIM. Nun, Konstanze, denkst du meinem Begehren nach? Der Tag ist bald verstrichen. Morgen mußt du mich lieben, oder–

KONSTANZE. Muß? Welch albernes Begehren! Als ob man die Liebe anbefehlen könnte wie eine Tracht Schläge! Aber freilich, wie ihr Türken zu Werke geht, läßt sich's auch allenfalls befehlen. Aber ihr seid wirklich zu beklagen. Ihr kerkert die Gegenstände eurer Begierden ein und seid zufrieden, eure Lüste zu büßen.

SELIM. Und glaubst du etwa, unsere Weiber wären weniger glücklich als in euren Ländern?

KONSTANZE. Die nichts besseres kennen!

SELIM. Auf diese Art wäre wohl keine Hoffnung, daß du je anders denken wirst.

Third Scene

Constanza. Selim.

SELIM: (sternly) Well, Constanza, I have allowed you too much time already. The day will soon be spent. Tomorrow you must give me your love or–

CONSTANZA: As if one could command love! I will honour you, yes, but love, never!

SELIM: And you do not tremble before the power I have over you?

SELIM: (furiously) No!–Not death, but tortures unabating!

KONSTANZE. Herr! Ich muß dir frei gestehen, denn was soll ich dich länger hinhalten, mich mit leerer Hoffnung schmeicheln, daß du dich durch mein Bitten erweichen ließest, ich werde stets so denken wie jetzt; dich verehren, aber-- lieben? Nie!

SELIM. Und du zitterst nicht vor der Gewalt, die ich über dich habe?

KONSTANZE. Nicht im geringsten. Sterben ist alles, was ich zu erwarten habe, und je eher dies geschieht, je lieber wird es mir sein.

SELIM. Elende! Nein! Nicht sterben, aber Martern von allen Arten –

KONSTANZE. Auch die will ich ertragen; du schreckst mich nicht, ich erwarte alles.

No. 11- ARIA

f
p
fp
fp
fp
fp
fp
fp
fp
fp
fp
p
cresc.
f
p
f

Constanze
C.
Mar-tern al-ler Ar-ten, al-ler Ar-ten mö-gen mei- - ner war-ten, ich ver-
Tor-tures un-a-ba-ting, un-a-ba-ting, may for me be waiting, I shall
p
cresc.
sfp
la-che, ich ver-la-che, ich ver-la- - - - - - - - - - - -
welcome, I shall welcome, I shall wel-
f
p
- - - - - - - - - - - -che Qual und Pein.
come woe and pain.
fp
f
Nichts, nichts, nichts, nichts soll mich er-
No fear, no force can e-v-er
f
sfp
schüt-tern, nur dann, nur dann würd' ich zit-tern, wenn ich
hurt me a-lone, my cour-age would de-sert me if I

un- - treu, un- - - treu. un - treu könn - te sein, nur
ev- er ev- er ev-er were un-true one
dann, dann würd' ich zit- - tern, wenn ich un- - treu könn - te
fear a-lone could hurt me if I ev- - -er were un-
sein, könn-te sein. Lass dich be- we- gen,
true, were un- true. Let mer-cy- sway- you,
p dolce
fp
ver- - schone mich, des Himmels Se-gen be-loh-ne
spare me,—my—Lord, and Heavens' blessing be your re-
dich, des Himmels Se-gen be-loh-ne dich, des Himmels Se- - - - -
ward and Heavens' blessing be your re-ward and Heavens' bless - - - -

gen, des
ing, and
Him-mels Se-gen be-loh-ne dich, des Him- mels
Heavens' bless-ing be your re-ward and Hea- vens'
Se- gen be-loh- ne, be-loh-ne.
bless ing for-ev- er be your re-
tr
dich, des Him-mels Se-gen be-loh-ne dich, be-loh-
ward, and Heavens' blessing, be your re-ward, your own
ne dich, be-loh-
re-ward. your own

ne, be-loh-ne dich!
your own re-ward.
cresc.
fp
Lass dich be-we-gen, ver-scho-ne
Let mer-cy sway you, spare me
mich,
lord.
des Him-mels
and Hea-vens'
Se-gen be-loh-ne dich,
bless-ing be your re-ward,
be-loh-ne dich!
your own re-ward.

Allegro assai.
Doch dich rührt kein Fle-hen, doch dich rührt kein Fle-hen,
But you—have de-cid-ed but you have de-cid-ed.
stand-haft, sollst du se-hen, duld' ich je-de Qual und Noth, duld' ich je-de
Wil-ling, clear-ly guid-ed I a-wait what has to be, I a-wait no
Qual, je-de Qual und Noth. Ord-ne nur, ge-
grace, no grace for me. Or-der then, com-
bie-te, ord-ne nur, ge-bie-te, dro-he, stra-fe,
mand me, or-der then, com-mand me, clam-or, threaten,
wü-the, zu-letzt be-freit mich doch der Tod. zu-letzt be-
pun-ish at last in death I shall be free, at last in
f
fp
pp
cresc.
sf
sfp
p
Viol.

C.
freit mich doch der Tod, der Tod, zuletzt be-freit mich doch der
death I shall be free, in death, at last in death I shall be
Tod, zuletzt be-freit mich doch der Tod.
free, at last in death I shall be free.
Tempo I
Laß dich be-we-gen, ver-scho-ne
Let mer-cy sway you spare me, my
mich, des Himmels Se-gen be-loh-ne dich, des Himmels Se-gen be-loh-ne
lord and Heavens' blessing be your re-ward and Heavens' blessing be your re-
dich, des Himmels Se
ward and Heavens' bless

C.
tr
gen be - loh - ne dich, des Himmels Se
ing be your re-ward and Heavens' bless
f
p
gen, des Him - mels Se - gen be - loh - ne dich, des
ing and Hea - vens' bless - ing be your re-ward, and
Him mels Se
Hea vens' bless
gen
ing
fp

be - loh - - - - - - ne
be your re-
Allegro assai
dich. Doch du bist ent-schlossen, doch du bist ent-schlos-sen,
ward. But you have de-cid-ed, but you have de-cid-ed.
wil-lig, un-ver-dros-sen wähl ich je-de Pein und Not, wähl ich je - - de
wil-ling, clear-ly guid-ed I a-wait what has to be I a-wait - no
Pein, je-de Pein und Not. Ord-ne nur, ge-
grace, no grace for me. Or-der then, com-
bie-te, ord-ne nur, ge-bie-te, lär-me, to-be,
mand me, or-der then, com-mand me, pun-ish, clam-or,
wü-te, zu-letzt be-freit mich doch der Tod, zu-letzt be-
threaten, at last in death I shall be free, at last in

C.
freit mich doch der Tod. der Tod. zu-letzt be-freit mich doch der
death I shall be free, in death; at last in death I shall be
Tod, zu-letzt be - freit
free, in death at last
mich doch der Tod. zu-letzt be - freit
I shall be free, in death at last
mich doch der Tod.
I shall be free.
der Tod! (entfernt sich) (exit)
be free.
sfp
f
p
cresc.

Vierter Auftritt

Blonde. Pedrillo.

PEDRILLO. Bst, bst! Blondchen! Ist der Weg rein?

BLONDE. Komm nur, komm! Der Bassa ist wieder zurück. Und meinem Alten habe ich eben den Kopf ein bißchen gewaschen. Was hast du denn?

PEDRILLO. O Neuigkeiten, Neuigkeiten, die dich entzücken werden.

BLONDE. Nun? Hurtig heraus damit!

PEDRILLO. Erst, liebes Herzens-Blondchen, laß dir vor allen Dingen einen recht herzlichen Kuß geben; du weißt ja, wie gestohlnes Gut schmeckt.

BLONDE. Pfui, pfui! Wenn das deine Neuigkeiten alle sind—

PEDRILLO. Närrchen, mach darum keinen Lärm, der alte spitzbübische Osmin lauert uns sicher auf den Dienst.

BLONDE. Nun? Und die Neuigkeiten?

PEDRILLO. Sind, daß das Ende unserer Sklaverei vor der Tür ist. (Er sieht sich sorgfältig um.) Belmonte, Konstanzes Geliebter, ist angekommen, und ich hab ihn unter dem Namen eines Baumeisters hier im Palast eingeführt.

BLONDE. Ah, was sagst du? Belmonte da?

PEDRILLO. Mit Leib und Seele!

BLONDE. Ha, das muß Konstanze wissen! (Will fort.)

PEDRILLO. Hör nur, Blondchen, hör nur erst Er hat ein Schiff hier in der Nähe in Bereitschaft, und wir haben beschlossen, euch diese Nacht zu entführen.

BLONDE. O allerliebst, allerliebst! Herzens-Pedrillo, das verdient einen Kuß! Geschwind, geschwind zu Konstanze! (Will fort.)

PEDRILLO. Halt nur, halt, und laß erst mit dir reden. Um Mitternacht kommt Belmonte mit einer Leiter zu Konstanzes Fenster, und ich zu dem deinigen, und dann geht's heidi davon!

BLONDE. O vortrefflich! Aber Osmin?

PEDRILLO. Hier ist ein Schlaftrunk für den alten Schlaukopf, den misch ihm fein manierlich ins Getränk, verstehst du? Ich habe dort auch schon ein Fläschchen angefüllt. Geht's hier nicht, wird's dort wohl gehen.

BLONDE. Sorg nicht für mich! Aber kann Konstanze ihren Geliebten nicht sprechen?

PEDRILLO. Sobald es vollends finster ist, kommt er hier in den Garten. Nun geh und bereite Konstanze vor; ich will hier Belmonte erwarten. Leb wohl, Herzchen, leb wohl!

BLONDE. Leb wohl, guter Pedrillo! Ach, was werd ich für Freude anrichten!

Fourth Scene

Blonda. Pedrillo.

PEDRILLO: (enters calling into the distance in a loud whisper) Pst, pst, Blonda! Is the way clear?

BLONDA: (appearing from other side of the stage) It is. But what is the matter?

PEDRILLO: Oh news, news that will delight you!

BLONDA: Well, hurry, tell me.

PEDRILLO: First, dearest Blonda, let me give you a nice big kiss! You know, don't you, how forbidden fruit tastes? (they embrace)

BLONDA: (eagerly) Well, and the news?

PEDRILLO: The end of our slavery is at hand! Belmonte, Constanza's beloved, has arrived, and I have introduced him into the palace as an architect.

BLONDA: Oh, marvelous, marvelous! Precious Pedrillo, that deserves another kiss! (she kisses him) Now I must tell Constanza right away!

PEDRILLO: Wait, let me explain to you first. I am giving Osmin a sleeping potion. I'll mix it into his evening drink. See there? I brought two bottles of wine with me. Then, when he is fast asleep, at the stroke of midnight, we'll come and abduct you and Constanza.

BLONDA: Wonderful! Oh, I am so excited! Good-bye, Pedrillo! - Oh, how happy I shall make Constanza!

No. 12- ARIA

Allegro.
Blonde.
Bl.
Wel-che Won-ne, wel-che Lust regt sich nun in mei-ner
O what rapture, what de-light, makes my heart so gay and
Brust, wel-che Won-ne, wel-che Lust regt sich nun in mei-ner Brust! Vol- - ler
bright, o what rapture, what de-light, makes my heart so gay and bright. I must
Freu-den will ich springen, ihr die fro-he Nachricht bringen, und mit Lachen und mit
tell her when I see her that - Bel-mon-te came to free her and with gladness and with
Scherzen ih-rem schwachen, kran - ken Her-zen Trost und Ret-tung pro - phe-
laughter, end-ing sad-ness ev - er af-ter, joy and freedom pro - phe-

Bl.
zeih'n, Trost und Ret-tung pro-phe - zeih'n. Vol - ler Freuden will ich
sy, joy and freedom pro-phe- sy. Not a mo-ment can I
cresc.
f p
sprin-gen, ihr die fro - he Nach-richt brin-gen. und mit
lin- ger, hap-py tid-ings will I bring her, and with
La - chen und mit Scherzen ih - rem schwachen, kran-ken Her - zen, ih - rem schwachen, schwachen,
gladness and with laughter, ending sad- ness ev- er af-ter, end-ing sad- ness, ev - er,
kran - ken Her - - - - - zen Trost und Ret - tung pro - phe -
ev - er af- - - - - - ter, joy and free - dom pro - phe-
zeih'n, Trost und Ret- tung pro - phe - zeih'n, Trost und Ret-tung pro - phe -
sy, joy and free- dom pro - phe - sy, joy and free-dom pro - phe-
f fp

Bl.
zeihn, pro - phe - zeihn. Wel - che Won - ne, wel - che Lust regt sich nun in mei - ner
sy, pro - phe - sy. What a hap-py, hap-py day all our trou-bles fade a-
p
Brust, wel - che Won - ne, wel - che Lust regt sich nun in mei - ner Brust!
way, what a hap-py, hap-py day all our trou-bles fade a-way-
Vol - ler Freu - den will ich sprin - gen, ihr die fro - he Nach - richt
I must tell her when I see her that Bel-mon-te came to
brin - gen, und mit La - chen und mit Scherzen ih - rem schwa - chen, kran - ken
free her, and with glad-ness and with laughter, end-ing sad - ness ev - er
Her - zen Trost und Ret - tung pro - phe - zeihn, Trost und Ret - tung pro - phe - zeihn
af - ter, say that free-dom is in sight, say that free-dom is in sight.
fp
cresc.
f

Bl.
Vol- - ler Freu-den will ich springen, ihr die fro-he Nach-richt
Not a mo-ment can I lin-ger; hap - py tidings will I
brin-gen, und mit La-chen und mit Scher-zen ih-rem schwa-chen, kran-ken Her-zen, ih-rem
bring her, and with glad-ness, and with laughter, end-ing sad - ness ev - er af - ter, end-ing
schwa-chen, schwa-chen, kran-ken Her - - - - - - - zen Trost und
sad- ness ev - er, ev - er af - - - - - - - ter, joy and
Ret - tung pro - phe-zeih'n, Trost und Ret - tung pro - phe - zeih'n,
free - dom pro - phe- sy, joy and free - dom pro - phe - sy,
Trost und Ret - tung pro - - phe-zeih'n, Trost und Ret - tung
joy and free - dom pro - - phe- sy, joy and free - dom
cresc.

Fünfter Auftritt

(Pedrillo (allein).

PEDRILLO: Ah, dass es schon vorbei wäre! Dass wir schon auf offner See wären, unsre Mädels im Arm und dies verwünschte Land im Rücken hätten! Doch sei's gewagt; entweder jetzt oder niemals! Wer zagt, verliert!

Fifth Scene

Pedrillo (alone).

PEDRILLO: Ah, if it only were over! If we only were already on the open sea, our sweethearts in our arms and this cursed land behind us! Well, on to battle! Now or never! He who hesitates is lost!

No. 13- ARIA
Allegro con spirito.
Pedrillo.
Frisch zum Kampfe! frisch zum Streite!
Now or nev-er, now or nev-er!
Nur ein fei-ger Tropf ver-zagt, nur ein fei-ger Tropf ver-zagt.
He who hes-i-tates is lost, he who hes-i-tates is lost.
Sollt' ich zit-tern? sollt' ich za-gen? nicht mein Le-ben mu-thig
Should I rath-er. wait till la-ter would my chan-ces then be
wa-gen? nicht mein Le-ben mu-thig wa-gen?
great-er, should I rath-er wait til la-ter?

P.
Nein, ach nein, es sei ge - wagt! ach nein, nein, nein, es sei ge - wagt! nein,
No, ah no, the die is cast ah no, no, no, I shall the die is cast
es sei ge - wagt, es sei ge - wagt, es sei gewagt, es sei ge - wagt!
we must es-cape at an-y - cost we must es-cape at an-y cost.
fp
cresc.
f
Nur ein fei-ger Tropf ver - zagt, nur ein fei - ger Tropf ver - zagt.
He who hes-i-tates is lost, he who hes-i-tates is lost.
p
Sollt' ich zit - tern? sollt' ich za - gen? nicht mein Le - ben mu - thig
Had I bet-ter tell my mas-ter that we're head-ing for dis-
wa - gen? nicht mein Le - ben mu - thig wa-gen?
as-ter, that we're head-ing for dis-as-ter.

Nein, ach nein, es sei ge - wagt! ach nein, nein, nein, es sei ge - wagt! nein, es sei ge - wagt, es sei ge-wagt, es sei ge - wagt, es sei ge-wagt, es sei ge - wagt!
No, ah no, the die is cast! ah no, no, no, the die is cast! no, the die is cast, we must es-cape at an-y cost, we must es-cape at an-y cost!
fp
cresc.
f
Nur ein fei - ger Tropf ver - zagt, nur ein fei - ger Tropf ver - zagt.
He who hes-i-tates is lost, he who hes-i-tates is lost.
p
Frisch zum Kam-pfe! frisch zum Strei - te! frisch, frisch zum
Now or nev-er for the die is cast now or

Kam-pfe! frisch zum Strei- -te! frisch zum Kam- -pfe! frisch zum
nev-er, now or nev - er, now or nev-er, now or
Strei - - - - te!
nev - - - - er!
Nur ein fei-ger Tropf ver-zagt, nur ein fei-ger Tropf ver-
He who hes-i-tates is lost, he who hes-i-tates is
zagt! Frisch zum Strei-te! frisch zum Kam-pfe! frisch zum Strei-te!
lost. Now or nev-er, now or nev-er, now or nev-er.

Sechster Auftritt

Pedrillo. Osmin.

OSMIN: Ha! Geht's hier so lustig zu? Es muss dir verteufelt wohl gehen.

PEDRILLO: Ei, wer wird so ein Kopfhänger sein; es kommt beim Henker da nichts bei heraus! Das haben die Pedrillos von jeher in ihrer Familie gehabt. Fröhlickheit und Wein versüsst die härteste Sklaverei. Freilich könnt ihr armen Schlucker das nicht begreifen, dass es so ein herrlich Ding um ein Gläschen guten alten Lustigmacher ist. Wahrhaftig, da hat euer Vater Mahomet einen verzweifelten Bock geschossen, dass er euch den Wein verboten hat. Wenn das verwünschte Gesetz nicht wäre, du müsstest ein Gläschen mit mir trinken, du möchtest wollen oder nicht. (Für sich.) Vielleicht beisst er an: er trinkt ihn gar zu gern.

OSMIN: Wein mit dir? Ja, Gift —

PEDRILLO: Immer Gift und Dolch, und Dolch und Gift! Lass doch den alten Groll einmal fahren und sei vernünftig. Sieh einmal, ein paar Flaschen Cyperwein! Ah! (Er zeigt ihm zwei Flaschen, wovon die eine grösser als die andere ist.) Die sollen mir vortrefflich schmecken!

OSMIN: (Für sich). Wenn ich trauen dürfte?

PEDRILLO: Das ist ein Wein, das ist ein Wein! (Er setzt sich nach türkischer Art auf die Erde und trinkt aus der kleinen Flasche.)

OSMIN: Kost einmal die grosse Flasche auch.

PEDRILLO: Denkst wohl gar, ich habe Gift hinein getan? Ha, lass dir keine grauen Haare wachsen! Es verlohnte sich der Mühe, dass ich deinetwegen zum Teufel führe. Da sieh, ob ich trinke. (Er trinkt aus der grossen Flasche ein wenig.) Nun, hast du noch Bedenken? Traust mir noch nicht? Pfui, Osmin, sollst dich schämen! Da nimm! (Er gibt ihm die grosse Flasche.) Oder willst du die kleine?

OSMIN: Nein, lass nur, lass nur! Aber wenn du mich verrätst — (Sieht sich sorgfältig um.)

PEDRILLO: Als wenn wir einander nicht weiter brauchten. Immer frisch! Mahomet liegt längst auf'm Ohr und hat nötiger zu tun, als sich um deine Flasche Wein zu bekümmern.

Sixth Scene

Pedrillo. Osmin.

OSMIN: (entering) Ha, having a merry time here? Things must be going devilish well for you!

PEDRILLO: Why must you always be so grouchy? Look at me! Gaiety and wine sweeten the hardest slavery. Of course, you poor wretches could never understand that there is something so wonderful about a glass of the good old merrymaker! Truly, your Father Mohammed has made a desperate blunder when he forbade you wine. Were it not for that, you could have a little glass with me.

OSMIN: Wine with you? Why—poison—

PEDRILLO: —and daggers, and daggers and poison! Let your old grudge go for once and be sensible! Look here, two bottles of Cyprus wine. This is the mother— (he shows him the large bottle) —and this is the daughter. (he shows him the small one) They are going to taste wonderful to me. (he sits down on the ground in Turkish fashion and drinks a little from the small bottle)

OSMIN: (hesitant, but with interest) Taste the large bottle, too, why don't you?

PEDRILLO: You don't trust me? Shame on you! Look here, see me drink! (he pretends to drink from the large bottle) Now, you try! Here is the mother. (hands him the large bottle) Or do you want the daughter?

OSMIN: I prefer the mother. But if you betray me—

PEDRILLO: Betray you? As if we did not need each other in the future! Go to it! Mohammed has more important things to do than to concern himself about a bottle of wine.

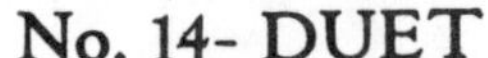

No. 14- DUET

Allegro.

p

Pedrillo.

Vi-vat Bacchus! Bacchus le-be! Bacchus war ein bra-ver Mann. Vi-vat Bac-chus! Bac-chus le-be! Bac-chus war ein bra-ver Mann.

Long live Bacchus, Bacchus prosper, Bacchus is the man for me. Long live Bacchus, Bacchus prosper, Bacchus is the man for me!

Osmin.

Ob ich's wa-ge? ob ich trin-ke? ob's wohl Al-lah se-hen kann?

Do I dare it? Dare I do it? Would not Al-lah look and see?

ad lib.

Pedrillo.

Was hilft das Zaudern? das Zaudern? Hin-un-ter! hin-un-ter! Nicht lan-ge, nicht lan-ge ge-

What use to dil-ly to dal-ly, Just down it, just down it, don't tar-ry, don't tarry, be

tr *sf* *p*

(drinks)
Osmin (trinkt).
P.
O.
fragt, nicht lan - ge, nicht lan - ge ge - fragt! Nun wär's ge - sche - hen! nun wär's ge -
brisk, don't tar-ry, don't tar-ry, be brisk! Now it is o-ver, now I have
cresc.
f
f p
f p
Pedr. Adagio.
Allegro.
Es le - ben die Mäd-chen, die
May long live the mai-dens, the
Osm.
sche - hen! Das heiss' ich, das heiss' ich ge - wagt. Es le - ben die Mäd - chen, die
done it! I call that, I call that a risk. May long live the mai- dens, the
Adagio.
Allegro.
p
Blon - den, die Braunen, die Blon - den, die Braunen! Sie le - ben, sie le - ben, sie
blonde ones, the dark ones, the blonde ones, the dark ones! May long live, may long live, may
Blon - den, die Brau - nen, die Blon - den, die Brau - nen! Sie le - ben, sie le - ben, sie
blonde ones, the dark ones. the blonde ones, the dark ones! May long live, may long live, may
le - ben hoch! sie le - ben, sie le - ben, sie le - ben hoch!
long live they, may long live, may long live, may long live they!
le - ben hoch! sie le - ben, sie le - ben, sie le - ben hoch!
long live they, may long live, may long live, may long live they!

ad lib.
P.
Das schmeckt trefflich!
What a fla-vour!
Ach! das heiss' ich Göt-ter-trank!
Ah, I call that heav-en-ly!
ad lib.
O.
Das schmeckt herr-lich!
What a savour!
Ach! das heiss' ich Göt-ter-trank! Vi-vat
Ah, I call that heav-en-ly! Long live
fp
fp
fp
p
Vi-vat Bacchus, Bacchus le-be, Bacchus,
Long live Bacchus, Bacchus prosper, Bacchus
Bacchus, Bacchus le-be, Bacchus, der den Wein er-fand! Vi-vat Bacchus, Bacchus le-be, Bacchus,
Bacchus, Bacchus prosper, Bacchus who in-vent-ed wine! Long live Bacchus, Bacchus prosper, Bacchus
f
der den Wein er-fand! Vi-vat Bac-chus! Bac-chus le-be!
who in-vent-ed wine! Long live Bacchus! Bac-chus pros-per!
der den Wein er-fand! Vi-vat Bac-chus! Bac-chus le-be!
who in-vent-ed wine! Long live Bacchus! Bac-chus pros-per!
sotto voce
Es le-ben die Mäd-chen, die Blon-den, die Brau-nen, sie le-ben
May long live the mai-dens, the blonde ones, the dark ones, may long live
Es le-ben die Mäd-chen, die Blon-den, die Brau-nen, sie le-ben
May long live the mai-dens, the blonde ones, the dark ones, may long live
p

P.
hoch! Vi-vat Bacchus! vi-vat, der den Wein er-fand! Vi-vat Bac-chus!
they! Long live Bacchus! Bacchus who in-vent-ed wine! Long live Bac-chus,
O.
hoch! Vi-vat, der den Wein er-fand! Vi-vat Bac-chus!
they! Bac-chus who in-vent-ed wine! Long live Bac-chus,
f
sotto voce
Bac-chus le-be! Es le-ben die Mäd-chen, die Blon-den, die
Bac-chus prosper! May long live the mai-dens, the blonde ones, the
sotto voce
Bac-chus le-be! Es le-ben die Mäd-chen, die Blon-den, die
Bac-chus prosper! May long live the mai-dens, the blonde ones, the
p
Brau-nen, sie le-ben hoch! Vi-vat Bac-chus! vi-vat, der den Wein er-fand! Vi-vat
dark ones, may long live they! Long live Bacchus, Bacchus who in-vent-ed wine, long live
Brau-nen, sie le-ben hoch! Vi-vat, der den Wein er-fand!
dark ones, may long live they! Bacchus who in-vent-ed wine!
Bacchus! vi-vat, der den Wein er-fand!
Bacchus, Bacchus who in-vent-ed wine!
Vi-vat, der den Wein er-fand!
Bacchus who in-vent-ed wine!

PEDRILLO. Wahrhaftig, das muß ich gestehen, es geht doch nichts über den Wein! Wein ist mir lieber, als Geld und Mädchen. Bin ich verdrießlich, mürrisch, launisch: hurtig nehm ich meine Zuflucht zur Flasche, und kaum seh ich den ersten Boden: weg ist all mein Verdruß! Meine Flasche macht mir kein schiefes Gesicht, wie mein Mädchen, wenn ihr der Kopf nicht auf dem rechten Fleck steht. Und schwatzt mir von Süßigkeiten der Liebe und des Ehestandes, was Ihr wollt: Wein auf der Zunge geht über alles!

OSMIN (fängt bereits an, die Wirkung des Weins und des Schlaftrunks zu spüren, und wird bis zum Ende des Auftritts immer schläfriger und träger, doch darf's der Schauspieler nicht übertreiben und muß nur immer halb träumend und schlaftrunken bleiben). Das ist wahr - Wein - Wein - ist ein schönes Getränk; und unser großer - Prophet mag mir's nicht übelnehmen - Gift und Dolch, es ist doch eine hübsche Sache um den Wein! - Nicht - Bruder Pedrillo?

PEDRILLO. Richtig, Bruder Osmin, richtig!

OSMIN. Man wird gleich so - munter (Er nickt zuweilen.) - so vergnügt - so aufgeräumt - Hast du nichts mehr, Bruder? (Er langt auf eine lächerliche Art nach einer zweiten Flasche, die Pedrillo ihm reicht.)

PEDRILLO. Hör du, Alter, trink mir nicht zu viel, es kommt einem in den Kopf.

OSMIN. Trag doch keine - Sorge, ich bin so - so - nüchtern wie möglich. - Aber das ist wahr, - (Er fängt an, auf der Erde hin und her zu wanken.) es schmeckt - vortrefflich!

PEDRILLO (für sich). Es wirkt, Alter, es wirkt!

OSMIN. Aber verraten mußt du mich nicht — Brüderchen - verraten - denn - wenn's Mahomet nein, nein - der Bassa wüßte - denn siehst du - liebes Blondchen - ja oder nein!

PEDRILLO (für sich). Nun wird's Zeit, ihn fortzuschaffen! (Laut.) Nun komm, Alter, komm, wir wollen schlafen gehn! (Er hebt ihn auf.)

OSMIN. Schlafen? - Schämst du dich nicht? Gift und Dolch! Wer wird denn so schläfrig sein - es ist ja kaum Morgen -

PEDRILLO. Ho, ho, die Sonne ist schon hinunter! Komm, komm, daß uns der Bassa nicht überrascht!

OSMIN (im Abführen). Ja, ja - eine Flasche - guter Bassa - geht über - alles! - Gute Nacht - Brüderchen - gute Nacht. (Pedrillo führt ihn hinein, kommt aber gleich wieder zurück.)

PEDRILLO: Truly, I must confess, there's nothing like wine! Wine is dearer to me than money and women.

OSMIN: (begins already to feel the effect of the wine and the sleeping potion. He becomes increasingly sleepy until the end of the scene. However, the actor must not exaggerate and must always remain half-dreaming and half-drunk) That is true—wine—wine—is a beautiful thing, and our great Prophet will not take it amiss—poison and daggers, wine is a great thing. Isn't it so, Brother Pedrillo?

PEDRILLO: Right, Brother Osmin, right.

OSMIN: One becomes so—lively. . . (he nods now and then) —so gay—so merry. Haven't you any more, Brother? (in a ridiculous way he reaches for a second bottle, which Pedrillo hands him).

PEDRILLO: Listen, old man, don't drink too much; it goes to the head.

OSMIN: Don't you worry, I—I am so—so sober as as can be. But you must not betray me, —Brother —for if Mohammed—no—no—the Pasha knew—you see—dear Blonda—yes or no!

PEDRILLO: (to himself) Now it's time to get him out of the way. (aloud) Now come on, old friend, let's go to sleep. (he lifts him up)

OSMIN: (in a daze) Sleep? Aren't you ashamed? Poison and daggers! Who's sleepy? It is early—

PEDRILLO: Ho ho! The sun has set already. Come, before the Pasha takes us by surprise.

OSMIN: (while being led away, mumbling) Yes, yes—a bottle—good Pasha—is better—than anything! Goodnight,—Brother—goodnight. (Pedrillo leads Osmin away, but returns immediately)

Siebenter Auftritt

Pedrillo. Hernach Belmonte, Konstanze, Blonde.

PEDRILLO (macht's Osmin nach). Gute Nacht-Brüderchen- gute Nacht! Hahahaha, alter Eisenfresser, erwischt man dich so? Gift und Dolch! Du hast deine Ladung! Nur fürcht ich, ist's noch zu zeitig am Tage; bis Mitternacht sind noch drei Stunden, und da könnt er leicht wieder ausgeschlafen haben.– Ach, kommen Sie, kommen Sie, liebster Herr! Unser Argus ist blind, ich hab ihn tüchtig zugedeckt.

BELMONTE. O daß wir glücklich wären! Aber sag: ist Konstanze noch nicht hier?

PEDRILLO. Eben kommt sie da den Gang herauf. Reden Sie alles mit ihr ab, aber fassen Sie sich kurz, denn der Verräter schläft nicht immer. (Während der Unterredung des Belmonte mit Konstanze unterhält sich Pedrillo mit Blonde, der er durch Pantomime den ganzen Auftritt mit dem Osmin vormacht und jenem nachahmt; zuletzt unterrichtet er sie ebenfalls, daß er um Mitternacht mit einer Leiter unter ihr Fenster kommen wolle, um sie zu entführen.)

KONSTANZE. O mein Belmonte!
BELMONTE. O Konstanze! } (Einander im Arm.)

KONSTANZE. Ist's möglich? Nach so viel Tagen der Angst, nach so viel ausgestandenen Leiden, dich wieder in meinen Armen.

BELMONTE. O dieser Augenblick versüßt allen Kummer, macht mich all meinen Schmerz vergessen.

KONSTANZE. Hier will ich an deinem Busen liegen und weinen! Ach, jetzt fühl ich's, die Freude hat auch ihre Tränen.

Seventh Scene

Pedrillo. Then Belmonte, Constanza, Blonda.

PEDRILLO: (imitating Osmin and laughing) Goodnight–Brother–goodnight. Poison and daggers, you have your cargo aboard!

BELMONTE: (entering) Pedrillo, is Constanza here yet?

PEDRILLO! She is just coming along the pathway.

CONSTANZA: (entering, followed by Blonda) Oh, my Belmonte!

BELMONTE: Oh, Constanza! (they rush into each other's arms)

CONSTANZA: Can it be true? After so many days of anxiety, after so many sufferings, you are in my arms again!

BELMONTE: Oh, this moment softens all grief, makes me forget all my sorrow.

CONSTANZA: Take me in your arms and let me weep. Ah, now I feel it–joy, too, has its tears!

No. 15 ARIA

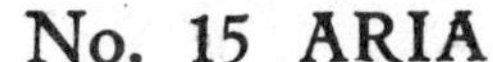

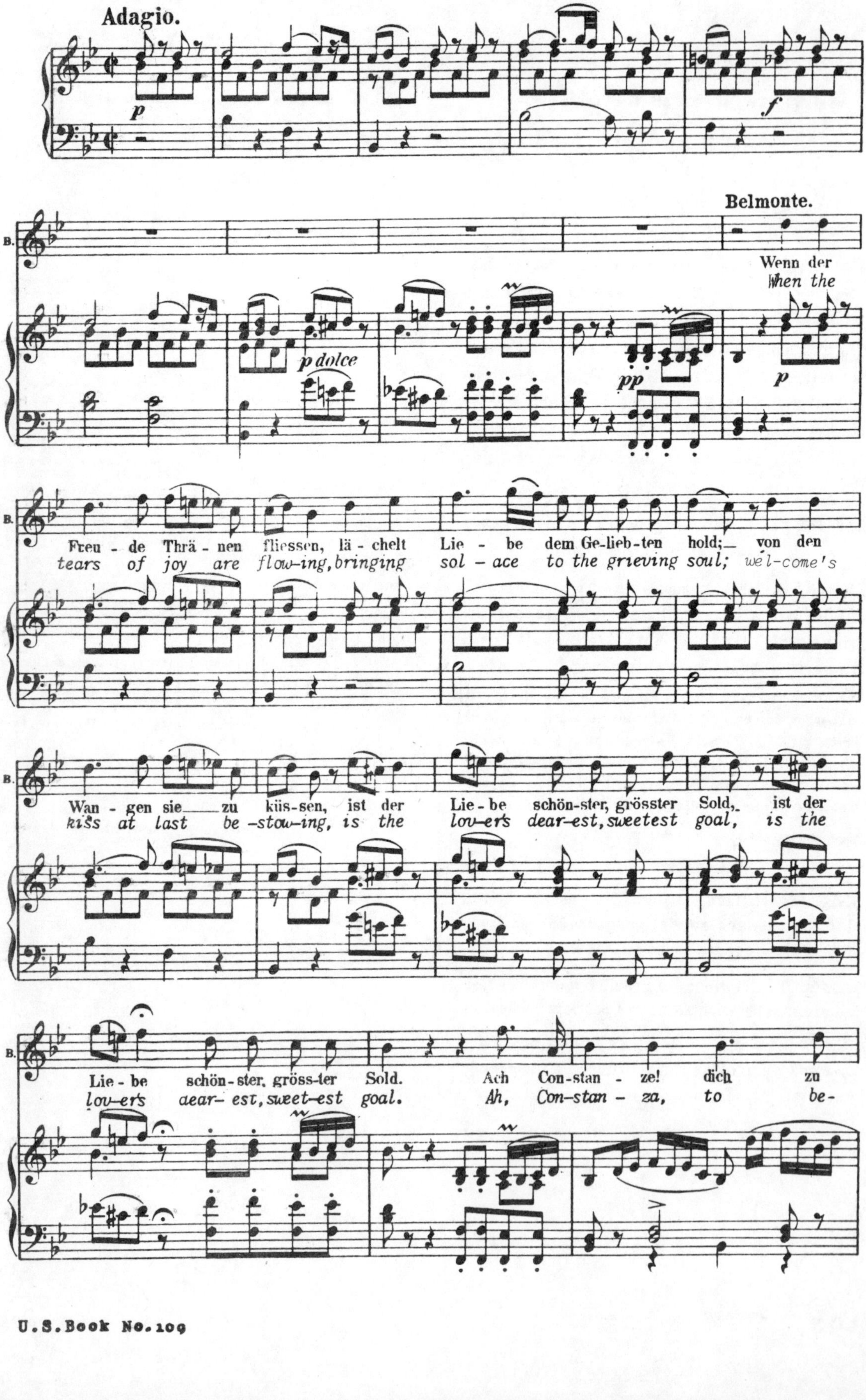
Adagio.
p
f
Belmonte.
B.
Wenn der
When the
p dolce
pp
p
Freu - de Thrä - nen fliessen, lä - chelt Lie - be dem Ge-lieb-ten hold; von den
tears of joy are flow-ing, bringing sol - ace to the grieving soul; wel-come's
Wan - gen sie zu küs-sen, ist der Lie-be schön-ster, grösster Sold, ist der
kiss at last be -stow-ing, is the lov-er's dear-est, sweetest goal, is the
Lie - be schön-ster, gröss-ter Sold. Ach Con-stan - ze! dich zu
lov-er's dear- est, sweet-est goal. Ah, Con-stan - za, to be-

B.
se - hen. dich voll Won - ne voll Ent - zü - cken an dies
hold you, full of won-der, to em- brace you, in my
trea - - - e Herz zu drü - cken, loh-net mir nicht Kron' und Pracht, loh-net
lov - - ing arms en - lace you, such a joy and such de-light. more I
mir nicht Kron' und Pracht, nicht Kron' und Pracht, loh-net mir nicht Kron' und
prize than fame and might, more than fame and might more I prize than fame and
Pracht! Wenn der Freu - de Thrä - nen fliessen, lä - chelt Lie - be dem Ge-lieb-ten
might! When the tears of joy are flowing, bringing sol - ace to the grieving
hold; von den Wan - gen sie zu küs-sen, ist der Lie - be schönster, grösster
soul; wel-come's kiss at last be - stowing, is the lov-er's dear-est, sweet-est
f
p

B.
Sold, ist der Lie-be schönster, grösster Sold. Ach Con-stanze! dich zu
goal, is the lov-er's dear-est, sweetest goal. Ah Con-stanza, to be-
sfp
sfp
sfp
sfp
se-hen, dich voll Won-ne, voll Ent-zü-cken an dies treu-e Herz zu drü-cken, loh-net
hold you, full of won-der, to em-brace thee, in my lov-ing arms en-lace thee, more I
sf
p
sf
p
cresc.
p
mir nicht Kron' und Pracht. lo - net mir
prize than fame and might, more - I prize
Allegretto.
tr
nicht Kron' und Pracht.
than fame and might.
sotto voce
Ha! die-ses sel'-ge Wie-der-fin-den lässt in-nig
Now that our lonely days are end-ed, have we pro-
fp

B.
erst mich ganz em - pfinden. wel-chen Schmerz die Tren - nung macht.
found-ly com-pre-hended, What des-pair the part - ing brings.
sfp
mf
B.
Ha! die-ses sel' - ge Wie - der-fin - den lässt in - nig erst mich
Now that our lone - ly days are end - ed, have we pro-found - ly
p
B.
ganz em-pfin - den, welchen Schmerz, welchen Schmerz die Trennung, die Tren-nung
com - pre-hend - ed, what des-pair, what des-pair the part-ing, the part-ing
sfp
sfp
sfp
B.
macht, welchen Schmerz die Trennung macht welchen Schmerz die Trennung
brings, what des - pair the part-ing brings, what des-pair the part-ing
sfp
B.
macht, die Tren - nung macht, die Tren - nung macht.
brings, the parting brings, the part-ing brings.
f

No. 16 QUARTET

B.
Nun muss al - ler Kum-mer schwinden, o wie ist mein Herz er-freut, mein
Now leave all your cares be-hind you, oh what bliss pervades my heart, per -
p
f
p
Const.
C.
Sich' die Freudenthrä-nen fliessen!
See the tears of joy are flow-ing!
B.
Herz er-freut! Hol - de, lass hin-weg sie
vades my heart! Let my kisses speed their
Viol.
C.
Dass es doch die letz-te sei, dass es
May this tear the last one be, May this
B.
küs-sen! Ja, noch heu-te wirst du frei, ja, noch heu -
go-ing! Yes, to - mor-row you'll be free, yes to mor -
C.
doch die letz - te, die letz - te sei, die letz-te sei!
tear the last one, the last one be, the last one be!
B.
- te, heu - te, heu - te wirst du frei, wirst du frei!
- row, yes to - mor - row you'll be free, you'll be free!
f

Pedrillo.
Al-so, Blondchen, hast's ver-standen? Al-les ist zur Flucht vor-
Now my Blond-a stead-y, stead-y, for escape the plans are
han-den. um Schlag zwöl-fe sind wir da, um Schlag zwöl-fe sind wir da
read-y; on the stroke of twelve we come, on the stroke of twelve we come.
Blonde.
Un-be-sorgt, es wird nichts feh-len, die Mi-nu-ten werd' ich
Have no fear, no more de-bat-ing, an-xiously I shall be
zählen, wär' der Au-genblick schon da, wär' der Au-genblick schon da!
waiting. Would the moment swiftly come, would the mo-ment swiftly come!
Const. Blonde.
End-lich scheint die Hoff-nungs-son-ne hell durch's
Bright at last the sun-light's glow-ing through the
Belm. Pedr.
End-lich scheint die Hoff-nungs-son-ne hell durch's
Bright at last the sun-light's glow-ing through the

C.
Bl.
trü - be, durch's trü - be Fir - ma - ment, hell durch's trü - be Fir - ma - ment.
gloom - y, the gloom - y heav - en rends, through the gloom - y heaven rends!
B.
P.
trü - be, durch's trü - be Fir - ma - ment, hell durch's trü - be Fir - ma - ment.
gloom - y, the gloom - y heav - en rends, through the gloom - y heaven rends!
f
sotto voce
Voll Ent - zücken, Freud' und Wonne seh'n wir
With en - chantment, rap - ture knowing, now all
Voll Ent - zücken, Freud' und Wonne seh'n wir
With en - chantment, rap - ture knowing, now all
p
un - srer Lei - den End', seh'n wir un - srer Leiden End'!
hope - less suff'ring ends, now all hope - less suff'ring ends!
un - srer Lei - den End', seh'n wir un - srer Leiden End'!
hope - less suff'ring ends, now all hope - less suff'ring ends!
f
p
Voll Ent - zücken, Freud' und
With en - chantment, rap - ture
Voll Ent - zücken. Freud' und
With en - chantment, rap - ture

C.
Bl.
Wonne seh'n wir un - srer Lei - den End'. seh'n wir un - srer Leiden
know-ing, now all hope - less suff'ring ends, now all hope- less suff'ring
B.
P.
Wonne seh'n wir un - srer Lei - den End', sehn wir un - srer Leiden
know-ing, now all hope- less suff'ring ends, now all hope-less suff'ring
End, seh'n wir un - srer Leiden End'!
ends, now all hope - less suff'ring ends!
Andante.
End, seh'n wir un - srer Leiden End'!
ends, now all hope - less suff'ring ends!
Andante.
Belm.
Doch ach! bei al-ler Lust em - pfin - det mei-ne Brust noch manch' ge-
And yet, I am op-pressed, for deep with-in my breast, there dwells a
Const.
Was ist es? Lieb - ster, sprich:
What is it? Dear - est, say?
ge-
Ex -
hei - me Sorgen.
troubled feeling.

schwind, erkläre dich,
plain without de-lay,
geschwind, erkläre dich, o halt'
ex-plain without de-lay, let no-
mir nichts ver - bor - gen, nichts ver - bor - gen, nichts ver - bor - gen!
thing be un- spok- -en, be un- spok -en, my be -lov-ed.
Belm.
Man sagt...
They say,
Viol.
man sagt...
they say,
du sei'st...
you are ...
Const.
Nun wei - ter!
Con-tin-ue!
Pedr.
Belmonte und Constanze (sehen einander stillschweigend und furchtsam an).
(look at each other silently and anxiously)
Doch Blondchen, ach! die
If I should risk the
Blonde.
Pedrillo (zeigt, dass er wage gehenkt zu werden).
(shows that he dares to be hung)
Hans Narr! schnappt's bei dir ü - ber? Ei,
You-fool! have you gone cra-zy? If
Lei - ter! bist du wohl so viel werth, wohl so viel werth?
gal-lows! Do you de-serve that risk, de-serve that risk?
sfp
sfp

Bl.
hät-test du nur lieber die Fra-ge umge-kehrt, die Frage, um-ge-kehrt!
some-one were to ask that, then I should be the one, then I should be the one.
P.
Doch Herr Os-min... doch Herr Os-
Is not Os-min,... is not Os-
fp
Blonde. Const. Belm.
P. Bl. C. B.
min... doch Herr Os-min... Lass hö-ren! Willst du dich nicht er-klä-ren? Man
min,... is not Os-min,... I'm list'n-ing Are you a-fraid to tell me? They
Const.
B. C.
sagt... du sei'st... Nun weiter?
say, you are Con-tinue?
Pedr. Blonde.
P. Bl.
Doch Herr Os-min... doch Herr Os-min... Lass hö-ren!
Is not Os-min. is not Os-min, Con-tin-ue!
Recit. Const. Belm. Andante.
C. B.
Willst du dich nicht er-klären? Ich will, doch zürne nicht, wenn
Are you a-fraid to tell me? Well, then but do not mind if
Pedr.
P.
Hat nicht Osmin et-wan. hat nicht Osmin et-
I ask you if Os-min- I ask you if Os-
Recit.
Andante.
sfp

ich nach dem Ge-rücht, das ich ge-hört, es wa-ge, dich
I re-peat to you what I have heard, and ask you the
wan, wie man fast glauben kann, sein Recht, sein Recht als Herr probi-ret, sein Recht als Herr pro-
min, as one has of-ten seen, has not his right as lord demanded, his right as lord de-
zit-ternd, be-bend fra-ge, ob du den Bas-sa
anxious, fear-ful ques-tion, are you the Pa-sha's
bi-ret und bei dir e-xer-ci-ret, e-xer-ci-ret? bei dir pro-bi-ret und e-xer-
mand-ed, and you to yield com-manded, yes, command-ed, his right de-manded his right de-
Const.
O wie du mich be-trübst!
O, how this wounds my heart!
liebst, den Bas-sa liebst?
love, the Pa-sha's love?
ci-ret? Dann wär's ein schlechter Kauf, dann wär's ein schlechter, schlechter Kauf!
manded? Then I had bargained dear, I bar-gained ver-y, ver-y dear!
Allegro assai.
Blonde (giebt ihm eine Ohrfeige.) gives him a box on the ear)
Pedr. (hält sich die Backe. (holds his cheek)
Belm. (knieend.) (kneeling)
Bl. P. B.
Da nimm die Antwort drauf! Nun bin ich auf-geklärt! Con-stanze, ach ver-gieb!
Here's what I have to say! Now I have seen the light! Con-stanza, pray for-give!

Blonde (zornig zu Pedrillo.)
(furiously to Pedrillo)
Const. (seufzend) (sighing)
Du bist mich gar nicht werth! Ob ich dir treu ver - blieb, ob ich dir treu ver - blieb?
I am too good for you! You doubt that I was true that I was true to you!
p
fp
Blonde. (zu Const.)
(to Const.)
Der Schlin-gel fragt gar an, ob ich ihm treu ge - blie - ben?
The ras- cal makes so bold, to think that I did fail him.
p
Const. (zu Blonde.)
(to Blonda)
Dem Bel - mont sag-te man, ich soll den Bas-sa
Bel- monte has been told, that I love Pa-sha
Pedr. (zu Belmonte)
(to Belmonte)
lie - ben! Dass Blon - de ehrlich sei, schwör'
Se - lim. That Blond- a has been true, I
Belm. (zu Pedrillo.)
(to Pedrillo)
ich bei al - len Teu - feln! Con - stan - ze ist mir treu, da - ran ist nicht zu
swear by my sal- va- tion. Con- stan-za's faithful too, to doubt were pro-fa-

Adagio.
Const.
Dem Bel-mont sag-te man, ich soll den Bas-sa lie-ben.
Bel-mon-te has been told, that I love Pa-sha Se-lim.
Blonde.
Der Schlingel fragt noch an, ob ich ihm treu ge-blie-ben?
The ras-cal makes so bold, to think that I did fail him.
Belm.
zweifeln. Con-stan-ze ist mir treu, da-ran ist nicht zu zwei-feln.
na-tion. Con-stan-za's faithful too, to doubt were pro-fa-na-tion.
Pedr.
Dass Blon-de ehr-lich sei, schwör' ich bei al-len Teu-feln.
That Blond-a has been true, I swear by my sal-va-tion.
Adagio.
Andantino
Const. Blonde.
Wenn unsrer Eh-re we-gen die
If men mis-trust our hon-or and
Belm. Pedr.
So-bald sich Weiber krän-ken, dass
If wo-men are of-fend-ed be-
Andantino
Männer Argwohn he-gen, ver-dächtig auf uns sehn, das ist nicht aus-zu-stehn, ver-
think that we de-ceive them, they're slight-ing our good name, it's they who are to blame, they're
wir sie un-treu den-ken, dann sind sie wahrhaft treu, von al-lem Vor-wurf frei, dann
cause we don't be-lieve them, they're put-ting us to shame and must be free from blame, they're

Allegretto.
C.
Bl.
dächtig auf uns sehn, das ist nicht aus - zu - stehn.
slight-ing our good name, It's they who are to blame.
Pedr.
B.
P.
sind sie wahrhaft treu, von al - lem Vor - wurf frei. Liebstes Blond-chen! ach ver-
put-ting us to shame, and must be free from blame. Dearest Blond - a, ah for -
Allegretto.
p
P.
zei - he, sieh', ich bau' auf dei - ne Treu - e mehr jetzt als auf mei - nen
give me, in your faith I am be - liev-ing, more in - deed than in my
Blonde.
Bl.
Nein! das kann ich dir nicht schenken, nein, das kann ich dir nicht
No. no more shall you a - buse me, no, no more shall you a -
Belm.
P.
B.
Kopf. Ach Con - stan - ze! ach mein Le - ben! könn - test du mir doch ver -
soul. Ah, Con - stan - za, ah be - lieve me, if you on - ly will for -
Const.
C.
Bel - mont!
Bel - monte!
Bl.
schenken, mich mit so was zu ver - denken, mit dem al - ten dummen Tropf! Das kann ich dir nicht
buse me, so unjustly to ac - cuse me, with that pompous silly fool! No more shall you a -
B.
ge - ben, dass ich die - - se Fra - ge that.
give me, for this wrong I will a - tone.

C.
wie, du konn - test glauben, Bel - mont! wie, du konn - test glauben, dass man
see you are mis - tak - en, Bel - mont, see, you are mis - tak - en, that from
Bl.
schenken, nein, das kann ich dir nicht schenken, nein! mich mit so was zu ver-
buse me, Pedr. no, no more shall you a - buse me, no! So unjustly to ac -
P.
Lieb - stes Blondchen! ach ver - zei - he!
Dear - est Blonda! Ah for - give me!
Const.
dir dies Herz kann rau - ben, das nur dir, das nur
you my heart was tak - en, for it beats, for it
Blonde.
denken, mit dem al - ten dummen Tropf; nein, das kann ich dir nicht schenken, mich mit so was zu ver-
cuse me, with that pompous silly fool, no, no more shall you a - buse me, so un - justly to ac -
mfp
mfp
Const.
dir, das nur dir ge - schla - gen hat, das nur
beats, for it beats for you a - lone, for it
Blonde.
denken, mit dem al - ten dummen Tropf, mit dem al - ten dummen Tropf! Nein, das kann ich dir nicht
cuse me, with that pompous silly fool, with that pompous sil - ly fool! No, no more shall you a -
Belm.
B.
Ach Con -
Ah Con -
Pedr.
Liebstes Blondchen!
Dear - est Blonda!
mfp

C.
dir, das nur dir, das nur dir ge - schla - - gen
beats, for it beats, for it beats for you a -
Bl.
schenken, mich mit so was zu ver - denken, mit dem al - ten dummen Tropf, mit dem al - ten dummen
buse me, so un-just-ly to ac-cuse me, with that pompous silly fool, with that pompous sil-ly
B.
stan - ze! ach mein Le - ben!
stan- za! Ah be - lov - ed!
P.
ach ver-zei - he!
Ah forgive me!
mfp
C.
hat. das nur dir ge - schla - - gen hat?
lone, for it beats for you a - lone.
Bl.
Tropf, mit dem al - ten dummen Tropf, mit dem al - ten dum-men Tropf!
fool, with that pompous sil - ly fool, with that pompous sil - ly fool!
cresc.
p
Belm.
Pedr.
B.
P.
Ach ver - zei - - he! Ach ver - zei - - he!
Ah for - give me! Ah for - give me!
f
Fag.
Belm.
Pedr.
Ich be - reu - - e! Ich be - reu - - e!
See my griev - ing! See my griev - ing!
f p
fp

Const.
Ich ver - zei - he, ver - zei - he dei - ner Reu - - e.
I be-lieve, I be-lieve you, I for - give you!
Const. Blonde.
Wohl, es sei nun
Done with all dis-
Blonde.
Ich ver - - zei - he dei - ner Reu - - e.
I be - lieve you, I for - give you!
Belm. Pedr.
Wohl, es sei nun
Done with all dis -
fp
p
ab - - ge - - than, wohl, es sei nun ab - ge -
trust and blame, done, with all dis - trust and
f
Quart.
Allegro
than!
blame!
Const.
Es le - - - be die Lie - - -
Let love be our lead - - -
Const. Blonde.
be! Es le - - - be die Lie - - - be, es
er, let love be our lead - - - er, let
Belm.
Es
Let

C.
Bl.
le - - - be die Lie - - - be, die Lie - - - - - - -
love be our lead - - - er, our lead - - - - - - -
Belm. Pedr.
B.
P.
le - - - be die Lie - - - be! Es le - - - be die
love be our lead - - - er, let love - - be our
be, es le - be die Lie-be, nur sie sei uns theu-er! Nichts fa - che das
er, let love be our lead-er, our dear - est pos-session. May nev - er the
Lie-be, es le - be die Lie-be. nur sie sei uns theu-er!
leader, let love be our lead-er. our dear - est pos-session.
Const.
Feu - er der Ei - fersucht an, nichts, nichts, nichts
fu - ry of jeal- ous-y flame, no, no, may
Blonde.
Bl.
Feu - er der Ei - fersucht an, nichts, nichts, nichts, nichts
fu - ry of jeal- ous-y flame, no, no, no, may
Belm.
Nichts fa - che das Feu - er der Ei - fersucht an,
May nev - er the fu - ry of jeal - ous-y flame,
Pedr.
Nichts fa - che das
May nev - er the

C.
Bl.
B.
P.
fa - - che das Feu - er der Ei - fersucht an! Es
nev - - er the fu - ry of jeal-ous-y flame! Let
fa - - che das Feu - er der Ei - fersucht an! Es
nev - - er the fu - ry of jeal-ous-y flame! Let
nichts fa - che das Feu - er der Ei - fersucht an! Es
may nev - er the fu - ry of jeal-ous-y flame! Let
Feu - er der Ei - fersucht an, der Ei - fersucht an! Es
fu - ry of jeal - ous-y flame, of jeal-ous-y flame! Let
p
Const. Blonde.
le - be die Lie-be, nur sie sei uns theuer, nichts fa - che das Feu - er der
love be our lead-er, our dear - est pos-session, May nev - er the fu - ry of
Belm. Pedr.
le - be die Lie-be, nur sie sei uns theuer, nichts fa - che das Feu - er der
love be our lead-er, our dear - est pos-session, May nev - er the fu - ry of
cresc.
Ei - fersucht an, nichts fa - che das Feu - er der Ei - fersucht an! Nichts
jeal - ous-y flame, may nev - er the fu - ry of jeal - ous-y flame! May
Ei - fersucht an, nichts fa - che das Feu - er der Ei - fersucht an!
jeal - ous-y flame, may nev - er the fu - ry of jeal - ous-y flame!
f

Const.
C.
fa - che das Feu - er der Ei - fersucht an. nichts, nichts,
nev - er the fu - ry of jeal - ous-y flame, no, no,
Blonde.
Bl.
fa - che das Feu - er der Ei - fersucht an. nichts, nichts,
nev - er the fu - ry of jeal - ous-y flame, no, no,
Belm.
B.
Nichts fa - che das Feu - er der Ei - fersucht
May nev - er the fu - ry of jeal- ous-y
Pedr.
P.
Nichts
May
nichts fa - - che das Feu - er der Ei - fersucht an!
may nev - - er the fu - ry of jeal-ous - y flame!
nichts, nichts fa - - che das Feu - er der Ei - fersucht an!
no may nev - - er the fu - ry of jeal-ous- y flame!
an, nichts fa - che das Feu - er der Ei - fersucht an!
flame, may nev - er the fu - ry of jeal-ous- y flame!
fa - che das Feu - er der Ei - fersucht an, der Ei - fersucht an!
nev - er the fu - ry of jeal - ous- y flame, of jeal-ous - y flame!
Const.
p
Es le - be die Lie - be, es
Let love be our lead - er, let
Blonde.
p
Es le - be die
Let love be our
Belm.
p
Es
Let
p

C.
le - - be die Lie- - be, es le - be die Liebe, nur
love be our leader, let love be our leader, our
Bl.
Lie- - - be, die Lie- - - be, es le - be die Liebe, nur
lead - er, our lead - er, let love be our leader, our
B.
le - - be die Lie- - - be, es le - be die Liebe. nur
love be our lead - er, let love be our leader, our
Pedr.
P.
Es le- - - be die Lie - be, die Liebe, nur
Let love be our lead - er, our leader, our
Const. Blonde.
C.
Bl.
sie sei uns theuer, nichts fa - che das Feu - er der Ei - fersucht an, nichts
dear - est pos-session, may nev - er the fu - ry of jeal - ous-y flame, may
Belm. Pedr.
B.
P.
sie sei uns theuer, nichts fa - che das Feu - er der Ei - fersucht an, nichts
dear - est pos-session, may nev - er the fu - ry of jeal - ous-y flame, may
cresc.
fa - che das Feu - er der Ei - fersucht an, nichts, nichts, nichts,
nev - er the fu - ry of jeal - ous - y flame, no, no, no,
fa - che das Feu - er der Ei - fersucht an, nichts, nichts, nichts,
nev - er the fu - ry of jeal - ous - y flame, no, no, no,

Ende des zweiten Actes.
(End of the second act)

DRITTER AUFZUG

THIRD ACT

Platz vor dem Palast des Bassa Selim; auf einer Seite der Palast des Bassa, gegenüber die Wohnung des Osmin, hinten Aussicht aufs Meer. Es ist Mitternacht.

(Square in front of Pasha Selim's palace; on one side the Pasha's palace opposite Osmin's dwelling, in the background the view of the sea. It is midnight.)

Erster Auftritt

First Scene

Pedrillo. Klaas (der eine Leiter bringt).

Pedrillo. Klaas (bringing a ladder.)

PEDRILLO. Hier, lieber Klaas, hier leg sie indes nur nieder und hole die zweite vom Schiff. Aber nur hübsch leise, daß nicht viel Lärm gemacht wird, es geht hier auf Tod und Leben.

KLAAS. Laß mich nur machen, ich versteh das Ding auch ein bißchen; wenn wir sie nur erst an Bord haben.

PEDRILLO. Ach, lieber Klaas, wenn wir mit unsrer Beute glücklich nach Spanien kommen, ich glaube, Don Belmonte läßt dich in Gold einfassen.

KLAAS. Das möchte wohl ein bißchen zu warm aufs Fell gehn; doch das wird sich schon geben. Ich hole die Leiter. (Geht ab.)

PEDRILLO. Ach, wenn ich sagen sollte, daß mir's Herz nicht klopfte, so sagt ich eine schreckliche Lüge. Die verzweifelten Türken verstehn nicht den mindesten Spaß; und ob der Bassa gleich ein Renegat ist, so ist er, wenn's aufs Kopfab ankommt, doch ein völliger Türke (Klaas bringt die zweite Leiter.) So, guter Klaas, und nun lichte die Anker und spanne alle Segel auf, denn eh eine halbe Stunde vergeht, hast du deine völlige Ladung.

KLAAS. Bring sie nur hurtig, und dann laß mich sorgen. (Geht ab.)

PEDRILLO: (to Klaas, who brings a ladder) So, my dear Klaas, just put the ladder down here. But don't make any noise, it is a matter of life and death. (to Klaas puts the ladder against the balcony and goes back to his ship)

Zweiter Auftritt

Belmonte. Pedrillo.

PEDRILLO. Ach, ich muß Atem holen!-Es zieht mir's Herz so eng zusammen, als wenn ich's größte Schelmstück vorhätte!- Ach, wo mein Herr auch bleibt!

BELMONTE (ruft leise). Pedrillo! Pedrillo!

PEDRILLO. Wie gerufen!

BELMONTE. Ist alles fertig gemacht?

PEDRILLO. Alles! Jetzt will ich ein wenig um den Palast herum spionieren, wie's aussieht. Singen Sie indessen eins. Ich habe das so alle Abende getan; und wenn Sie da auch jemand gewahr wird, oder Ihnen begegnet, denn alle Stunden macht hier eine Janitscharenwache die Runde, so hat's nichts zu bedeuten, sie sind das von mir schon gewohnt; es ist fast besser, als wenn man Sie so still hier fände.

BELMONTE. Laß mich nur machen, und komm bald wieder. (Pedrillo geht ab.)

Second Scene

Belmonte. Pedrillo.

PEDRILLO: Ah, I must catch my breath, But where is my master?

BELMONTE: (entering, calls softly) Pedrillo, Pedrillo.

PEDRILLO: Just on time.

BELMONTE: Is everything ready?

PEDRILLO: Everything. Now I'll go and see how things look.

BELMONTE: (Pedrillo leaves) Come back soon.

Dritter Auftritt

Belmonte (allein).

BELMONTE. O Konstanze, Konstanze, wie schlägt mir das Herz! Je näher der Augenblick kommt, desto ängstlicher zagt meine Seele; ich fürchte und wünsche, bebe und hoffe. O Liebe, sei du mei ne Leiterin!

Third Scene

Belmonte (alone).

BELMONTE: Oh, Constanza, Constanza, how my heart is throbbing! The nearer the moment comes, the more anxious I am!

No. 17 - ARIA

Andante.
Belmonte.
Ich bau-e ganz auf dei-ne Stär-ke, ver-
I build my faith u-pon your pow-er, oh
trau', o Lie-be, dei-ner Macht, ver-trau', o Lie-be, o
love, con-fid-ing in your might, oh love, con-fid-ing, con-
Lie-be, dei-ner Macht. Denn
fid-ing in your might. Through

ach! was wurden nicht für Wer-ke schon oft durch dich — zu Stand' gebracht, was
you my hope be-gan to flow-er, you lead my way — as guid-ing light my
wur- den nicht für Werke schon oft — durch dich, zu Stand' gebracht!
hopes began to flow-er, you lead my way as guid-ing light
Was al - l r Welt un - mög - lich scheint, wird durch die Lie - be
A cause the world con-sid-ers vain, will love's a-chieving
doch vereint, wird durch die Lie-be, durch die Lie-be doch ver - eint, —
proud -ly gain, will love's a - chieving, love's a- chieving proud-ly gain,
wird durch die Liebe, durch die Liebe doch ver - eint,
will love's a-chieving, love's a-chieving proudly gain,

B.
doch ver - eint, doch ver -
proud - ly gain, proud-ly
eint, doch ver - eint.
gain, proud-ly gain.
Was al - ler Welt un - mög-lich scheint, wird
A cause the world consid-ers vain, will
durch die Lie - be doch ver - eint.
love's a-chiev - ing proud - ly gain.

Was al - ler Welt. al-ler
A cause the world, the
Welt un-möglich scheint, wird durch die Lie - be, durch die
world con-siders vain, will love's a - chiev - ing, love's a -
Lie-be doch ver - eint.
chieving proud-ly gain!
fp
Ich bau-e ganz auf dei - ne Stär - ke, ver-trau', o Lie - be, dei - ner
I build my faith u - pon your pow - er, oh Love, con - fid-ing in your,
p
mfp
Macht, ver - trau', o Lie - be, o Lie - - be, dei - ner Macht.
might, oh love, con - fid - ing, con-fid - ing in your might.
mfp

B.
Denn ach! was wur-den nicht für Wer-ke schon
Through you my hopes be-gan to flow-er. you
p
oft durch dich zu Stand' ge-bracht, schon oft durch dich zu Stand' ge-
lead my way as guid-ing light. You lead my way as guid-ing
bracht,
light.
schon oft, schon oft durch dich zu
You lead, you lead my way as

Vierter Auftritt

Belmonte. Pedrillo.

PEDRILLO: Alles liegt auf dem Ohr; es ist alles so ruhig, so stille als den Tag nach der Sündflut.

BELMONTE: Nun, so lass uns sie befreien. Wo ist die Leiter?

PEDRILLO: Nicht so hitzig. Ich muss erst das Signal geben.

BELMONTE: Was hindert dich denn, es nicht zu tun? Mach fort.

PEDRILLO: (Sieht nach der Uhr.) Eben recht, Schlag zwölf. Gehen Sie dort an die Ecke, und geben Sie wohl acht, dass wir nicht überrascht werden.

Fourth Scene

Belmonte. Pedrillo.

PEDRILLO: Everything is asleep. It is as still as on the day of the great flood. (returning, carrying a mandolin)

BELMONTE: Well, then, let us start, Where is the ladder?

PEDRILLO: Not so hasty! First I must give the signal.

BELMONTE: Then hurry! (he exits)

PEDRILLO: (looks at his watch) Just right. The stroke of twelve. (takes up his mandolin and begins to accompany)

BELMONTE: Zaudre nur nicht! (Geht ab.)

PEDRILLO: (Indem er seine Mandoline hervorholt.) Es ist doch um die Herzhaftigkeit eine erzläppische Sache. Wer keine hat, schafft sich mit aller Mühe keine an! Was mein Herz schlägt! Mein Papa muss ein Erzpoltron gewesen sein. (Fängt an zu spielen.) Nun, so sei es denn gewagt! (Singt und akkompagniert sich.)

te das Mädchen sehr, juch! rief er: wag' ich Kopf und Ehr', wenn ich sie ret - ten
woe and did ex- claim; "fain will I risk my life and fame to save the maid - en
Noch geht alles gut, es rührt sich noch nichts.
kann, wenn ich sie ret - ten kann.
dear to save the maid- en dear!''
Still everything goes smoothly, Nothing has stirred as yet.
BELMONTE: (Kommt hervor.) Mach ein Ende, Pedrillo.
PEDRILLO: An mir liegt es nicht, dass sie sich noch nicht zeigen. Entweder schlafen sie fester als jemals, oder der Bassa ist bei der Hand. Wir wollen's weiter versuchen. Bleiben Sie nur auf Ihrem Posten. (Belmonte geht wieder fort.)
BELMONTE: (Comes forward) Hurry, Pedrillo
PEDRILLO: It is not my fault that they are late. We shall try again. Just stay at your post. (Belmonte withdraws again)
„Ich komm' zu dir in finst'-rer Nacht, lass, Liebchen, husch mich ein; ich fürchte
"I come to thee in dark-est night, oh dear-est, hark to me; I have no
we-der Schloss noch Wacht, holla, horch auf! um Mit - ter-nacht sollst du er - lö - set
fear of lock or might, when all is still this ver-y night. I'll come to set thee

P.
sein. sollst du er - lö - set sein."
free, I'll come to set thee free."
P.
Ge-sagt, ge - than! Glock zwöl - fe stand der
Now said, then done! At twelve's com - mand the
P.
tapf're Rit - ter da, sanft reicht sie ihm die wei - che Hand, früh man die
va-liant knight was there. She gave to him her heart and hand, next morn the
P.
lee - re Zel - le fand, fort war sie hop - sa - sa, fort
cell did emp - ty stand, and flown the maid - en fair, and
P.
war sie hop - sa - sa!
flown the maid- en fair!

PEDRILLO. Sie macht auf, Herr, sie macht auf!

BELMONTE. Ich komme, ich komme!

KONSTANZE (oben am Fenster). Belmonte!

BELMONTE. Konstanze, hier bin ich; hurtig die Leiter! (Pedrillo stellt die Leiter an Konstanzes Fenster, Belmonte steigt hinein; Pedrillo hält die Leiter.)

PEDRILLO. Was das für einen abscheulichen Spektakel macht. (Hält die Hand aufs Herz.) Es wird immer ärger, weil es nun Ernst wird. Wenn sie mich hier erwischten, wie schön würden sie mit mir abtrollen, zum Kopfabschlagen, zum Spießen oder zum Hängen. Je nu, der Anfang ist einmal gemacht, jetzt ist's nicht mehr aufzuhalten, es geht nun schon einmal aufs Leben oder auf den Tod los!

BELMONTE (kommt mit Konstanze unten zur Tür heraus). Nun, holder Engel, nun hab ich dich wieder, ganz wieder! Nichts soll uns mehr trennen.

KONSTANZE. Wie ängstlich schlägt mein Herz, kaum bin ich imstande, mich aufrecht zu halten; wenn wir nur glücklich entkommen!

PEDRILLO. Nur fort, nicht geplaudert, sonst könnt es freilich schief gehen, wenn wir da lange Rat halten und seufzen! (Stößt Belmonte und Konstanze fort.) Nur frisch nach dem Strande zu! Ich komme gleich nach. (Belmonte und Konstanze ab.)

PEDRILLO. Nun, Kupido, du mächtiger Herzensdieb, halte mir die Leiter und hülle mich samt meiner Gerätschaft in einen dicken Nebel ein! (Er hat unter der Zeit die Leiter an Blondes Fenster gelegt und ist hinaufgestiegen.) Blondchen, Blondchen, mach auf, um Himmels willen, zaudre nicht, es ist um Hals und Kragen zu tun! (Es wird das Fenster geöffnet, er steigt hinein.)

PEDRILLO: (excitedly) She is opening the window, master—

BELMONTE: Constanza, Constanza!

CONSTANZA: (at the window) Belmonte!

BELMONTE: Wait for me inside! (to Pedrillo) Quickly the ladder! (Pedrillo places the ladder at Constanza's window; Belmonte climbs up, while Pedrillo holds the ladder)

PEDRILLO: What a horrible noise that makes! If they caught me now, they'd cut my head off in no time.

BELMONTE: Now, dearest angel, nothing shall ever part us any more. (comes out with Constanza through the door below) (they run off)

PEDRILLO: (while putting the ladder at Blonda's window) Blonda, Blonda, open, in Heaven's name! Hurry up, our necks are at stake! (the window is opened and he slips inside)

Fünfter Auftritt

Osmin. Ein Stummer.

(Osmin und ein schwarzer Stummer öffnen die Tür von Osmins Haus, wo Pedrillo hineingestiegen ist. Osmin, noch halb schlaftrunken, hat eine Laterne. Der Stumme gibt Osmin durch Zeichen zu verstehen, daß es nicht richtig sei; daß er Leute gehört habe usw.)

OSMIN. Lärmen hörtest du? Was kann's denn geben? Vielleicht Schwärmer? Geh, spioniere, bringe mir Antwort. (Der Stumme lauscht ein wenig herum; endlich wird er die Leiter an Osmins Fenster gewahr, erschrickt und zeigt sie Osmin, der wie im Taumel, mit der Laterne in der Hand an seine Haustür gelehnt, steht und nickt.) Gift und

Fifth Scene

Osmin. A mute.

(Osmin and a black mute open the door of Osmin's house, where Pedrillo has climbed in.) Osmin, still half asleep, holds a lantern. The mute gives Osmin to understand through signs that something is wrong, that he has heard people, etc.)

OSMIN: Noise you heard? What can it be, after all? Revelers perhaps? Go investigate, bring me an answer. (The mute looks about a little; finally he notices the ladder at Osmin's window, is startled and shows it to Osmin) Poison and

Dolch! Was ist das? Wer kann ins Haus steigen? Das sind Diebe oder Mörder. (Er tummelt sich herum; weil er aber noch halb schlaftrunken ist, stößt er sich hier und da.) Hurtig, hole die Wache! Ich will unterdessen lauern. (Der Stumme ab; Osmin setzt sich auf die Leiter, mit der Laterne in der Hand, und nickt ein. Pedrillo kommt rückwärts wieder zum Fenster herausgestiegen und will die Leiter wieder herunter.)

BLONDE (oben am Fenster, wird Osmin gewahr und ruft Pedrillo zu). O Himmel, Pedrillo, wir sind verloren!

PEDRILLO (sieht sich um, und sowie er Osmin gewahr wird, stutzt er, besieht ihn und steigt wieder zum Fenster hinein). Ach, welcher Teufel hat sich wider uns verschworen!

OSMIN (auf der Leiter dem Pedrillo nach, ruft). Blondchen, Blondchen!

PEDRILLO (im Hineinsteigen zu Blonde). Zurück, nur zurück!

OSMIN (steigt wieder zurück). Wart, Spitzbube, du sollst mir nicht entkommen. Hilfe! Hilfe! Wache! Hurtig, hier gibt's Räuber, herbei, herbei! (Pedrillo kommt mit Blonde unten zur Haustür heraus, sieht schüchtern nach der Leiter und schleicht sich dann mit Blonde darunter weg.)

PEDRILLO, BLONDE (im Abgehen). O Himmel steh uns bei, sonst sind wir verloren!

OSMIN. Zu Hilfe, zu Hilfe! Geschwind! (Er will nach.)

WACHE (mit Fackeln, halten Osmin auf). Halt, halt! Wohin?

OSMIN. Dorthin, dorthin.

WACHE. Wer bist du?

OSMIN. Nur nicht lange gefragt, sonst entkommen die Spitzbuben. Seht ihr denn nicht? Hier ist noch die Leiter.

WACHE. Das sehn wir; kannst nicht du sie angelegt haben?

OSMIN. Gift und Dolch! Kennt ihr mich denn nicht? Ich bin Oberaufseher der Gärten beim Bassa. Wenn ihr noch lange fragt, so hilft euer Kommen nichts. (Ein Teil der Wache bringt Pedrillo und Blonde zurück.) Ah endlich! Gift und Dolch! Seh ich recht! Ihr beide? Warte, spitzbübischer Pedrillo, dein Kopf soll am längsten festgestanden sein.

daggers! What is that? Who climbed into the house? It's robbers and murderers! (he staggers around, but because he is still drowsy, he bumps into various things) Hurry, bring the guard! I will keep watch in the meantime. (the mute runs off) (Osmin sits down on the ladder and falls into a doze. Pedrillo comes down, backwards, from the window, and is about to climb down the ladder again)

BLONDA: (above at the window, notices Osmin and calls Pedrillo) Heavens, Pedrillo, we are lost!

PEDRILLO: (turns around, and as soon as he sees Osmin, stops short and climbs into the window again) Who the devil has betrayed us?

OSMIN: (climbs on the ladder after Pedrillo, calls) Blonda, Blonda! (climbing halfway down again) Guards! Hurry! Robbers! Thieve! (Pedrillo comes out of the house with Blonda, looks furtively at the ladder, and steals away with Blonda)

PEDRILLO: (in going) Let's run for our lives!

OSMIN: (he wants to follow them) Help! Help! Guards!

GUARD: (with torches, holds Osmin back) Halt! Which way?

OSMIN: That way!

GUARD: Who are you?

OSMIN: Don't you know me? I am the head overseer of the Pasha's gardens. (a few of the guards bring Pedrillo and Blonda back) Ah, at last! Do I see right? Both of you?

PEDRILLO. Brüderchen, Brüderchen, wirst doch Spaß verstehn? Ich wollt dir dein Weibchen nur ein wenig spazieren führen, weil du heute dazu nicht aufgelegt bist. Du weißt schon (Heimlich zu Osmin.) wegen des Cyperweins.

OSMIN. Schurke, glaubst du mich zu betäuben? Hier verstehe ich keinen Spaß; dein Kopf muß herunter, so wahr ich ein Muselmann bin.

PEDRILLO. Und hast du einen Nutzen dabei? Wenn ich meinen Kopf verliere, sitzt deiner um so viel fester? (Ein anderer Teil der Wache, auch mit Fackeln, bringt Belmonte und Konstanze.)

BELMONTE (widersetzt sich noch). Schändliche, laßt mich los!

WACHE. Sachte, junger Herr, sachte! Uns entkommt man nicht so geschwinde.

OSMIN. Sieh da, die Gesellschaft wird immer stärker! Hat der Herr Baumeister auch wollen spazieren gehen! O ihr Spitzbuben! Hatte ich heute nicht recht, (Zu Belmonte.) daß ich dich nicht ins Haus lassen wollte? Nun wird der Bassa sehen, was für sauberes Gelichter er um sich hat.

BELMONTE. Das beiseite! Laß hören, ob mit euch ein vernünftig Wort zu sprechen ist? Hier ist ein Beutel mit Zechinen, er ist euer, und noch zweimal so viel; laßt mich los.

KONSTANZE. Laßt euch bewegen!

OSMIN. Ich glaube, ihr seid besessen? Euer Geld brauchen wir nicht, das bekommen wir ohnehin; eure Köpfe wollen wir. (Zur Wache.) Schleppt sie fort zum Bassa!

BELMONTE. } KONSTANZE. } Habt doch Erbarmen, laßt euch bewegen!

OSMIN. Um nichts in der Welt! Ich habe mir längst so einen Augenblick gewünscht. Fort, fort! (Die Wache führt Belmonte und Konstanze fort, samt Pedrillo und Blonde.)

PEDRILLO: (wheedling) But brother, little brother! You can understand a joke, can't you? I just wanted to take your little wife for a walk—because you were not in the mood for it today. You know, don't you? Because of the Cyprus wine. Remember the mother and daughter?

OSMIN: Scoundrel! Do you think you can make a fool of me? In this I don't understand any joke. Your head must come off, as sure as I as Osmin! (other guards, also carrying torches, bring back Belmonte and Constanza)

BELMONTE: (still resisting) Let go of me!

GUARD: Easy, young man! From us you don't escape so quickly!

OSMIN: See this! The party keeps getting larger and larger! Did Mr. Architect also wish to go for a walk?

BELMONTE: Here is a purse of gold pieces. It is yours, if you let us go.

CONSTANZA: Have mercy!

OSMIN: I believe you are mad! We don't need your money. That we shall get anyway. We want your heads! (to the guards) Drag them away to the Pasha!

BELMONTE: Have pity!

OSMIN: For nothing in the world! This is the moment I have been waiting for! (the guards lead Constanza, Belmonte, Pedrillo and Blonda away)

No. 19- ARIA
Allegro vivace.
Osmin.
O! wie will ich tri-um-
O what joy to see you
phi - ren, wenn sie euch zum Richt-platz füh - ren, und die Häl-se schnüren
fel-lows, swing -ing high up-on the gal-lows, with a rope a-round your
zu, schnüren zu, und die Häl-se schnüren zu, schnüren zu,
neck pull-ing tight, with a rope a-round your neck pull-ing tight.
schnüren zu, und die Häl-se schnüren zu, schnüren zu.
what a sight, with a rope a-round your neck pull-ing tight.

O.
Hü - pfen will ich, la - chen, sprin - gen, und ein
I shall jump and roar with laugh-ter and re-
Freu - den lied - chen sin - gen: denn nun hab'
joice for - ev - er af - ter, for this is
ich vor euch Ruh', denn nun hab'
the end of you, for this is
ich vor euch Ruh'.
the end of you.

O! wie will. ich tri-um-phi - ren, wenn sie euch zum Richtplatz füh - ren,
O what joy to see you fel-lows swing- ing high up- on the gal-lows
und die Hälse schnüren zu, schnüren zu, und die Häl-se schnüren zu, schnüren
with a rope a-round your neck pull-ing tight. with a rope a-round your neck pull-ing
zu. Schleicht nur säu-ber-lich und lei-se, ihr ver-damm-ten Ha-rems-Mäu-se,
tight. Just sneak clev-er-ly and light-ly, mice that prowl the ha-rem night-ly,
un - ser Ohr ent-deckt euch schon; und eh' ihr uns könnt ent-
for the walls have ears and eyes; and be-fore you look a-
springen, seht ihr euch in unsern Schlingen, und er-haschet eu-ren Lohn, und er-
round you, will my trust-y spies surround you, and you reap your rightful prize, and you
fp
sfp

O.
ha - schet eu - - ren Lohn.
reap - your right - ful prize.
Schleicht nur säu-ber-lich und lei-se, ihr ver-damm-ten Ha-rems-Mäu-se,
Just sneak clev-er-ly and light-ly, mice that prowl the ha-rem night-ly,
un-ser Ohr ent-deckt euch schon, ent-deckt euch schon, ent-deckt euch schon.
for the walls have ears and eyes, have ears and eyes, have ears and eyes.
fp
O! wie will ich tri-um-phi-ren, wenn sie euch zum Richt-platz
O what joy to see you fel-- lows swing- ing high up- on the
füh-ren, und die Häl-se schnü-ren zu, schnü-ren zu.
gal-- lows with a rope a-round your neck pull-ing tight

und die Häl-se schnüren zu. schnüren zu. Hü-pfen will ich,
with a rope a-round your neck, pull-ing tight. While you dan-gle - -
lachen, springen, und ein Freu - - - - - den -
ha, ha - - I will jump with joy - - - - and
lied-chen sin -
roar, with laugh -
- gen,
ter
denn nun hab' ich vor euch Ruh'
for this is the end of you,

O.
denn nun hab' ich vor euch Ruh'.
for this is the end of you.
Ob.
O! wie will ich tri-um-phi-ren, wenn sie euch zum Richtplatz
O! what joy to see you fel-lows swing-ing high up-on the
füh-ren, und die Häl-se schnüren zu, schnüren zu, schnüren zu, schnüren.
gal-lows with a rope a-round your neck pull-ing tight, pull-ing tight, with a
schnüren, schnüren zu, schnüren, schnüren, schnüren, schnüren, schnüren, schnüren, schnüren
rope a-round your neck pull-ing, pull-ing, pull-ing, pull-ing, pull-ing, pull-ing, pull-ing,

zu, und die Häl-se schnü-ren zu, und die Häl-se schnü-ren
tight, with a rope a-round your neck, with a rope a-round your
cresc.
f p
zu, schnü-ren zu, schnü-ren zu, schnüren, schnü-ren, schnü-ren zu, schnü-ren,
neck, pull-ing tight, pull-ing tight, with a rope a-round your neck pull-ing,
schnüren, schnüren, schnüren, schnüren, schnüren, schnüren zu, und die Häl-se
pull-ing, pull-ing, pull-ing, pull-ing pull-ing, pull-ing tight. With a rope a-
cresc.
schnü-ren zu, und die Hälse schnüren zu, und die Hälse schnüren zu, schnüren zu, schnüren
round your neck, with a rope a-round your neck with a rope a-round your neck pull-ing tight, pull-ing
f
zu.
tight.
(geht ab.) (exit)

Change of Scene

Room of the Pasha

Sechster Auftritt

Selim (mit Gefolge). Hernach Osmin, Belmonte, Konstanze und Wache.

SELIM (zu einem Offizier). Geht, unterrichtet euch, was der Lärm im Palast bedeutet; er hat uns im Schlaf aufgeschreckt, und laßt mir Osmin kommen. (Der Offizier will abgehen, indem kommt Osmin, zwar hastig, doch noch ein wenig schläfrig.)

OSMIN. Herr, verzeih, daß ich es so früh wage, deine Ruhe zu stören!

SELIM. Was gibt's, Osmin, was gibt's? Was bedeutet der Aufruhr?

OSMIN. Herr, es ist die schändlichste Verräterei in deinem Palast —

SELIM. Verräterei?

OSMIN. Die niederträchtigen Christensklaven entführen uns — die Weiber. Der große Baumeister, den du gestern auf Zureden des Verräters Pedrillo aufnahmst, hat deine — schöne Konstanze entführt.

SELIM. Konstanze? Entführt? Ah, setzt ihnen nach!

OSMIN. O, s'ist schon dafür gesorgt! Meiner Wachsamkeit — hast du es zu danken, daß ich sie wieder beim Schopf gekriegt habe. Auch mir selbst hatte der — spitzbübische Pedrillo eine gleiche Ehre zugedacht, und er hatte mein Blondchen schon beim Kopf, um mit ihr — in alle Welt zu reisen. Aber Gift und Dolch, er soll mir's entgelten! Sieh, da bringen sie sie! (Belmonte und Konstanze werden von der Wache hereingeführt.)

SELIM. Ah, Verräter! Ist's möglich? Ha, du heuchlerische Sirene! War das der Aufschub, den du begehrtest? Mißbrauchtest du so die Nachsicht, die ich dir gab, um mich zu hintergehen?

Sixth Scene

Selim (with suite), afterwards Osmin, Belmonte, Constanza and guard.

SELIM: (to an officer) Go and investigate the uproar in the palace. (officer starts to leave)

OSMIN: (entering, hastily, but still a bit sleepy) Lord, forgive me for having disturbed your rest. . but . . .

SELIM: What is it, Osmin?

OSMIN: Lord, the most shameful treachery. . .

SELIM: Treachery?

OSMIN: The great architect whom you engaged at the persuasion of Pedrillo has abducted Constanza!

SELIM: (furiously) Constanza? Ah, they must be pursued!

OSMIN: Oh, that I have taken care of! Pedrillo, the scoundrel, has done me a similar honor, stealing my Blonda. . .Ah! See there, they are bringing them in. (Belmonte and Constanza are led in by the guards)

SELIM: Traitors! and you, Constanza, was that the reason for the delay for which you were pleading?

KONSTANZE. Ich bin strafbar in deinen Augen, Herr, es ist wahr; aber es ist mein Geliebter, mein einziger Geliebter, dem lang schon dieses Herz gehört. O nur für ihn, nur um seinetwillen fleht ich um Aufschub. O laß mich sterben! Gern, gern will ich den Tod erdulden; aber schone nur sein Leben —

SELIM. Und du wagst's, Unverschämte, für ihn zu bitten?

KONSTANZE. Noch mehr: für ihn zu sterben!

BELMONTE. Ha, Bassa! Noch nie erniedrigte ich mich zu bitten, noch nie hat dieses Knie sich vor einem Menschen gebeugt: aber sieh, hier lieg ich zu deinen Füßen und flehe dein Mitleid an. Ich bin von einer großen spanischen Familie, man wird alles für mich zahlen. Laß dich bewegen, bestimme ein Lösegeld für mich und Konstanze so hoch du willst. Mein Name ist Lostados.

SELIM (staunend). Was hör ich! Der Kommandant von Oran, ist er dir bekannt?

BELMONTE. Das ist mein Vater.

SELIM. Dein Vater? Welcher glückliche Tag, den Sohn meines ärgsten Feindes in meiner Macht zu haben! Kann was angenehmeres sein? Wisse, Elender, dein Vater, dieser Barbar, ist schuld, daß ich mein Vaterland verlassen mußte. Sein unbiegsamer Geiz entriß mir eine Geliebte, die ich höher als mein Leben schätzte. Er brachte mich um Ehrenstellen, Vermögen, um alles. Kurz, er zernichtete mein ganzes Glück. Und dieses Mannes einzigen Sohn habe ich nun in meiner Gewalt! Sage, er an meiner Stelle, was würde er tun?

BELMONTE (ganz niedergedrückt). Mein Schicksal würde zu beklagen sein.

SELIM. Das soll es auch sein. Wie er mit mir verfahren ist, will ich mit dir verfahren. Folge mir, Osmin, ich will dir Befehle zu ihren Martern geben. (Zu der Wache.) Bewacht sie hier.

CONSTANZA: I know I am guilty in your eyes. To him, my only beloved, this heart has been given for a long time. Oh let me die. . .only spare his life.

BELMONTE: Ah, Pasha, never before has this knee bent before anyone. But there I lie, at your feet, imploring pity. Designate a ransom price for Constanza, as high as you wish, I am of a great Spanish family, My name is Lostados, my father is the Commandant of Oran.

SELIM: (amazed) What do I hear! The son of my bitterest enemy in my power! Be it known to you that your father's relentless greed forced me to leave my native land. He took all my heritage—in short, he destroyed all my happiness. Tell me, were he in my place, what would he do?

BELMONTE: (completely broken) My destiny would be lamentable.

SELIM: And so it shall be. Follow me, Osmin. I shall give you orders for their torture. (Selim exits with his suite, leaving two guards to watch the prisoners)

Seventh Scene

No. 20-RECITATIVE AND DUET

Belm.
B.
See-le! Welch' hol - de Gü-te! Du flö-ssest
spirit! What end - less boun-ty! You give me
p sf p cresc. sf p
Trost in mein er-schüttert Herz! Du linderst mir den To-desschmerz, und ach!
strength to con-quer ev'-ry fear, You make me calm when death is near, and ah,
colla parte
sf
DUETT.
Andante.
ich rei-sse dich in's Grab! Ha! du soll-test für mich
I draw you to the grave! What mis-for-tune I have
f sf p
sf p
ster-ben, ach Con-stan - ze! kann ich's wa-gen, noch die Au - gen auf-zu-
brought you oh Con - stan - za, dare I face you, dare I beg you to for-
sf p
f p
schlagen? Ich be-rei - - te dir den Tod, ich be-rei - te dir den
give me? I a-lone have brought your doom. I a-lone have brought your
fp fp

Const.
C.
B.
Ach! für mich giebst du dein Leben, giebst du dein Leben; ich nur
Dear- est I have caused your ru-in, have caused your ru-in, I have
Tod!
fall!
zog dich in's Ver - der - ben, ich ich nur zog dich
doomed what most I cher-ish, I, I have doomed what
fp
in's Ver - der - ben, und ich soll nicht mit dir ster - ben, und ich
most I cher-ish, and with you I should not perish, and with
soll nicht mit dir ster - ben, ich soll nicht mit dir
you I should not per - ish, with you; I should not
ster - ben? Won - ne ist mir dies Ge - bot, Won - ne
per - ish? Joy - ful do I heed the call, joy - ful
p

Const.
ist mir dies Ge - bot.
do I heed the call.
Ach Ge - lieb - ter!
Ah be - lov-ed!
dir zu le - ben, war mein
your sal-va-tion was my
Belm.
Ach Ge - lieb - te!
Ah be - lov-ed!
dir zu le - ben, war mein
your sal-va-tion was my
Wunsch und all' mein Stre - ben, all' mein Stre - ben, all' mein Wunsch und all' mein
hope, was all my hope and as-pir - a - tion, was my hope and as - pir -
Wunsch und all' mein Stre - ben, all' mein Stre - ben, all' mein Wunsch und all' mein
hope, was all my hope and as-pir - a - tion, was my hope and as - pir -
sfp
sfp
sfp
Stre - ben!
a - tion!
Oh - ne dich ist's mir nur Pein, län - ger
Without you 'tis vain for me lon - ger
Stre - ben!
a - tion!
Oh - ne dich ist's mir nur
With-out you 'tis vain for
auf der Welt zu sein, län - ger, län - ger auf der Welt zu
in this world to be, lon-ger, lon-ger, in this world to
Pein, län - ger auf der Welt zu sein, län - ger auf der Welt zu
me, lon-ger in this world to be, lon-ger in this world to

vi-
C.
sein. län - ger, län - ger auf der Welt zu sein.
be, lon - ger. lon - ger in this world to be.
B.
sein. län - ger; län - ger auf der Welt zu sein. Ha! du
be, lon - ger lon - ger in this world to be. For Bel-
f
C.
Ach! für mich giebst du dein Leben, du dein Leben.
Dear-est I have caused your ru-in, caused your ru-in,
B.
solltest für mich sterben! Ach! Con-
monte you must perish! Ah! Con-
f p f p cresc. p
C.
Ich nur
I have
B.
stan - ze, kann ich's wagen, noch die Au - gen auf - zu - schla - gen?
stan - za, dare I face you. dare I beg you, to for - give me?
C.
zog dich in's Ver - derben, und ich soll nicht mit dir sterben? Won - ne
doomed what most I cherish, and with you I should not perish? Joy - ful
B.
Ich be - rei - te dir den Tod,
I alone have brought your doom.
fp fp fp fp f p

C.
ist mir dies Ge - bot, Won - ne, Won - ne ist mir dies Ge - bot.
do I heed the call joy - ful, joy - ful do I heed the call.
B.
ich be - rei - te dir den Tod!
I a - lone have brought your doom.
f
p
C.
Ach Ge - lieb - ter! Dir zu le - ben, war mein Wunsch, war mein
Ah be - lov - ed, Your sal - va - tion was my hope, was my
B.
Ach Ge - lieb - te! Dir zu le - ben, war mein Wunsch, war mein
Ah be - lov - ed! Your sal - va - tion was my hope, was my
Viol.
Quart.
sfp
C.
Wunsch und all' mein Stre - ben, war mein Wunsch und all' mein Stre - ben; ohne
hope and as - pi - ra - tion, was my hope and as - pi - ra - tion; without
B.
Wunsch und all' mein Stre - ben, war mein Wunsch und all' mein Stre - ben;
hope and as - pi - ra - tion, was my hope and as - pi - ra - tion;
sfp
de
C.
dich ist's mir nur Pein, län - ger auf der Welt zu sein.
you 'tis vain for me lon - ger in this world to be.
B.
oh - ne dich ist's mir nur Pein, län - ger auf der Welt zu
without you 'tis vain for me lon - ger in this world to

C.
oh-ne dich ist's mir nur Pein, ist's mir nur Pein, län - ger auf der Welt zu sein.
without thee 'tis vain for me, 'tis vain for me lon - ger in this world to be.
B.
sein, oh-ne dich ist's mir nur Pein. län - ger auf der Welt zu sein.
be. without thee 'tis vain for me lon - ger in this world to be.
Allegro.
Mu - - - thig
Calm I
Ich will al - les ger - ne lei - den,
Glad - ly all I shall be bearing,
Allegro.
p
sterb' ich, und mit Freuden, weil ich dir zur Sei - - te bin, weil ich
perish, and un - car-ing, for with you I do a - bide, for with
weil ich dir zur Sei - te bin, weil ich
for with you I do a-bide, for with
fp
dir zur Sei - - te bin, zur Sei - te bin.
you I do a - bide, I do a - bide.
dir zur Sei - - te bin, zur Sei - te bin.
you I do a - bide, I do a - bide.

C.
B.
Um dich, Ge - lieb - ter, geb' ich gern mein Le - ben hin,
For you, be - lov - ed, glad I cast my life a - side,
Um dich, Ge - lieb - te,
For you, be - lov - ed,
geb' ich gern mein Le - ben hin,
glad I cast my life a - side,
sf
geb' ich gern mein Le - ben hin.
glad I cast my life a - side.
O wel - che Se - ligkeit!
Oh won-drous happiness,
p
fp
O wel - che Se - ligkeit!
Oh won -drous happiness!
O wel - che Se -
Oh won-drous hap -
lig-
pi
cresc.
f

C.
keit! Mit dem Ge-lieb-ten ster-ben, ist se-li-ges Ent-zü-cken, mit won-nevol-len
ness! To die with the be-lov-ed is now a bless-ed mis-sion; with glo-ri-fy-ing
B.
keit! Mit der Ge-lieb-ten ster-ben, ist se-li-ges Ent-zü-cken, mit won-nevol-len
ness! To die with the be-lov-ed is now a bless-ed mis-sion; with glo-ri-fy-ing
fp
p
Blicken verlässt man da die Welt, ver-lässt man, ver-lässt man da die Welt!
vision we bid the world farewell: we bid then, we bid the world farewell!
Blicken verlässt man da die Welt, ver-lässt man, ver-lässt man da die Welt!
vision we bid the world farewell, we bid then, we bid the world farewell!
O wel-che Se-ligkeit! O wel-che Se-ligkeit! O wel-che
Oh wondrous happiness! Oh won-drous happiness! Oh won-drous
O wel-che Se-ligkeit! O wel-che Se-ligkeit! O wel-che
Oh wondrous happiness! Oh won-drous happiness! Oh won-drous
Se- lig-
hap- pi-
Se- lig-
hap- pi-
cresc
f

—de
C.
keit! Mit dem Ge-lieb-ten ster - ben. ist se - li-ges Ent - zü - cken. mit won - nevol - len
ness! To die with the be - lov - ed is now a blessed mis - sion;with glo-ri-fy-ing
B.
keit! Mit der Ge-lieb-ten ster - ben, ist se - li-ges Ent - zü - cken. mit won - nevol - len
ness! To die with the be - lov - ed is now a blessed mis - sion;with glo-ri-fy-ing
p
fp
fp
Blicken ver-lässt man da die Welt, ver - lässt man, ver - lässt man da die
vision we bid the world farewell, we bid then, we bid the world fare-
Blicken ver-lässt man da die Welt, ver - lässt man, ver - lässt man da die
vision we bid the world farewell, we bid then, we bid the world fare-
fp
fp
Welt, mit won-ne-vol-len
well, With glo-ri-fy-ing
Welt! Mit der Ge-lieb-ten ster - ben. ist se-li-ges Ent-zücken, mit won-ne-vol-len
well! To die with the be-lov - ed is now a blessed mission,With glo-ri-fy-ing
sf
p
fp
fp
Bli - cken ver-lässt man da die Welt, mit dem Ge-lieb-ten ster - ben, ist
vi - sion,we bid the world farewell! To die with the be - lov - ed, is
Bli - cken ver-lässt man da die Welt,
vi - sion,we bid the world fare-well!
f
p
sf
p

C.
se - li-ges Ent - zücken. mit won - ne-vol - len Bli - cken verlässt man da die Welt, mit
now a bless-ed mission.with glo-ri-fy-ing vi - sion we bid the world fare-well, with
B.
mit won - ne-vol - len Bli - cken verlässt man da die Welt, mit
with glo-ri-fy-ing vi - sion we bid the world fare-well, with
fp
f
p
C.
won - ne-vol-len Bli - cken verlässt man da die Welt, ver-lässt man
glo-ri-fy-ing vi - sion we bid the world fare-well, we bid the
B.
won - ne-vol - len Bli - cken ver-lässt man da die Welt, ver-lässt man
glo-ri-fy-ing vi - sion we bid the world fare-well. we bid the
C.
da die Welt, ver-lässt man da die Welt, die Welt, die
world fare-well, we bid the world fare-well, the world fare-
B.
da die Welt, ver-lässt man da die, Welt, die Welt, die
world fare-well, we bid the world fare-well, the world fare-
C.
Welt!
well!
B.
Welt!
well!

Achter Auftritt

(Pedrillo und Blonde werden von einem andern Teil der Wache hereingeführt)

PEDRILLO. Ach, Herr, wir sind hin! An Rettung ist nicht mehr zu denken. Man macht schon alle Zubereitungen, um uns aus der Welt zu schaffen. Es ist erschrecklich, was sie mit uns anfangen wollen! Ich, wie ich im Vorbeigehen gehört habe, soll in Öl gesotten und dann gespießt werden. Das ist ein sauber Traktament! Ach, Blondchen, Blondchen, was werden sie wohl mit dir anfangen?

BLONDE. Das gilt mir nun ganz gleich. Da es einmal gestorben sein muß, ist mir alles recht.

PEDRILLO. Welche Standhaftigkeit! Ich bin doch von gutem altchristlichen Geschlecht aus Spanien, aber so gleichgültig kann ich beim Tode nicht sein! Weiß der Teufel— Gott sei bei mir, wie kann mir auch jetzt der Teufel auf die Zunge kommen?

Eighth Scene

(Pedrillo and Blonda are led in by another part of the guard)

PEDRILLO: (Pedrillo and Blonda are led in by guards) Alas, Master, we are done for! There is no more hope of rescue. Already they are making all preparations to speed us out of the world. I am to be fried in oil and then put on the spit. Ah, dearest Blonda, what will they do to you, I wonder?

BLONDA: That is all the same to me now. Since dying must be done, I don't mind how.

PEDRILLO: What fortitude! I wish I could be so indifferent to death!

Neunter Auftritt

Selim. Osmin (voll Freuden) und Gefolge.

Die Vorigen.

SELIM. Nun, Sklave! Elender Sklave! Zitterst du? Erwartest du dein Urteil?

BELMONTE. Ja, Bassa, mit so vieler Kaltblütigkeit, als Hitze du es aussprechen kannst. Kühle deine Rache an mir, tilge das Unrecht, so mein Vater dir angetan; ich erwarte alles und tadle dich nicht.

Ninth Scene

Selim, Osmin (joyfully), and suite, enter.

SELIM: (Selim, Osmin (jomfully) and suite enter) Miserable slave! Are you trembling? Are you awaiting your sentence?

BELMONTE: Yes, Pasha, and with utmost calm. Revenge yourself, I expect no grace from you.

SELIM. Es muß also wohl deinem Geschlechte ganz eigen sein, Ungerechtigkeiten zu begehen, weil du das für so ausgemacht annimmst? Du betrügst dich. Ich habe deinen Vater viel zu sehr verabscheut, als daß ich je in seine Fußtapfen treten könnte. Nimm deine Freiheit, nimm Konstanze, segle in dein Vaterland, sage deinem Vater, daß du in meiner Gewalt warst, daß ich dich freigelassen, um ihm sagen zu können, es wäre ein weit größer Vergnügen, eine erlittene Ungerechtigkeit durch Wohltaten zu vergelten, als Laster mit Lastern tilgen.

BELMONTE. Herr! Du setzest mich in Erstaunen—

SELIM (ihn verächtlich ansehend). Das glaub ich. Zieh damit hin, und werde du wenigstens menschlicher als dein Vater, so ist meine Handlung belohnt.

KONSTANZE. Herr, vergib! Ich schätzte bisher deine edle Seele, aber nun bewundere ich—

SELIM. Still! Ich wünsche für die Falschheit, so Sie an mir begangen, daß Sie es nie bereuen möchten, mein Herz ausgeschlagen zu haben. (Im Begriff abzugehen.)

PEDRILLO (tritt ihm in den Weg und fällt ihm zu Füßen). Herr, dürfen wir beide Unglückliche es auch wagen, um Gnade zu flehen? Ich war von Jugend auf ein treuer Diener meines Herrn.

OSMIN. Herr, beim Allah, laß dich ja nicht von dem verwünschten Schmarotzer hintergehn! Keine Gnade! Er hat schon hundertmal den Tod verdient.

SELIM. Er mag ihn also in seinem Vaterlande suchen. (Zur Wache.) Man begleite alle vier an das Schiff. (Gibt Belmonte ein Papier.) Hier ist euer Paßport.

OSMIN. Wie, meine Blonde soll er auch mitnehmen?

SELIM (scherzhaft). Alter, sind dir deine Augen nicht lieb? Ich sorge besser für dich als du denkst.

OSMIN. Gift und Dolch! Ich möchte bersten.

SELIM. Beruhige dich. Wen man durch Wohltun nicht für sich gewinnen kann, den muß man sich vom Halse schaffen.

SELIM: You deceive yourself. You are a free man. Take Constanza and sail to your homeland. It is far greater pleasure for me to right a suffered injustice through a good deed, than to repay wickedness in kind.

BELMONTE: My lord, your generosity amazes me!

SELIM: That I believe. Go hence, and make Constanza happy, Thus my action will be rewarded. (starts to leave)

PEDRILLO: Lord, dare we two unhappy creatures also beg for grace? (steps into his way and falls to his feet)

OSMIN: By Allah, great Pasha, no grace for them! They have already deserved death a hundred times!

SELIM: Let them seek it then, in their homeland. (to the guard) Escort all four to the ship.

OSMIN: What! No my Blonda, too!

SELIM: (jokingly) Old man, are your eyes not dear to you?

OSMIN: Poison and daggers! I am going to explode!

No. 21-FINALE VAUDEVILLE

C.
selbst im Schoos der Lie-be, ver-ges-sen. was der Dank ge-beut. Mein Herz, der
time of love and pleasure, re-mem-ber gra-ti-tude's de-mands. My heart which
C.
Lie-be nun ge-weiht, hegt auch dem Dank ge-weih-te Trie-
love a-lone com-mands, un-dy-ing thanks will ev-er trea-
C.
be. Wer so viel Huld ver-ges-sen kann, den seh'man mit Ver-achtung
sure. He who such boun-ty can for-get, shall with dis-dain and scorn be
C. Bl.
an. Wer so viel Huld verges-sen kann, den seh'man mit Ver-achtung an.
met. He who such boun-ty can for-get, shall with disdain and scorn be met.
Pedrillo.
B. P.
Wer so viel Huld verges-sen kann, den seh'man mit Ver-achtung an. Wenn ich es
He who such boun-ty can for-get, shall with disdain and scorn be met. Should I for-
O.
Wer so viel Huld verges-sen kann, den seh'man mit Ver-achtung an.
He who such boun-ty can for-get, shall with disdain and scorn be met.
p

P.
je ver-ges - sen könn-te, wie nah' ich am Er - dros - seln war. und all' der
get then please re-mind me how near to slaugh- ter I was bound, and in what
P.
an - de-ren Ge - fahr, ich lief', als ob der Kopf mir brenn -
dan -gers we were found. Thank heav- -en I — leave them all be - hind —
P.
te. Wer so viel Huld ver-ges - sen kann, den seh' man mit Ver - ach-tung
me. He who such boun - ty can for- get, shall with dis-dain and scorn be
C.
Bl.
Blonde.
Wer so viel Huld verges - sen kann, den seh' man mit Ver - achtung an. Nehmt meinen
He who such boun- ty can for-get, shall with disdain and scorn be met. Lord Pa-sha,
B.
P.
an. Wer so viel Huld verges - sen kann, den seh' man mit Ver - achtung an.
met. He who such boun- ty can for-get, shall with disdain and scorn be met.
O.
Wer so viel Huld verges - sen kann, den seh' man mit Ver - achtung an.
He who such boun- ty can for-get, shall with disdain and scorn be met.
tr
f
p

Bl.
Dank mit tau-send Freuden, Herr Bassa! lebt ge-sund und froh! Osmin! das Schick-sal will es
Be as-sured that nev-er shall I for-get the thanks I owe. Osmin, Dame Fortune wills it
(auf Osmin zeigend.)
(pointing to Osmin)
so, ich muss von dir auf e-wig schei-den; wer so wie du nur zan-ken
so, that you and I must part for-ev-er; he who like you can scold and
Più Andante.
kann, den sieht man mit Ver-ach-tung an.
fret, shall with dis-dain and scorn be met.
Osmin.
O.
Ver-bren-nen soll-te man die Hun-de, die uns so
The shame-less dogs de-serve no quar-ter, for all their
Più Andante.
Allegretto.
schänd-lich hin-ter-geh'n; es ist nicht län-ger an-zu-seh'n, mir starrt die
crimes they have to-pay We must not wait a-noth-er day oh let me
Allegretto.

stringendo
Allegro assai.
Zun - ge fast im Mun - de, um ih - ren Lohn zu ord - nen an. Erst ge-
lead them to the slaugh - ter and let them die in my own way. You'll be
stringendo
fp
köpft, dann ge - han - gen, dann ge - spiesst auf hei - sse Stan - gen, dann ver-
hanged then be - head - ed, then be drowned, and then be shred - ded; on the
brannt, dann ge - bun - den und getaucht, zu - letzt ge - schunden! Erst ge - köpft, dann ge-
spit we will boil you and in oil at least we boil you You'll be hanged then be-
pp
hangen, dann ge - spiesst auf hei - sse Stangen, dann ver - brannt, dann ge - bunden und ge-
headed, then be drowned, and then be shredded; on the spit we will boil you and in
stacc.
cresc.
(läuft voll Wuth ab.) (runs away furiously)
taucht, zuletzt ge - schun - - den!
oil at last we boil you!
f

Andante sostenuto.

Const. / Blonde. (C. Bl.) — *sotto voce* — *f* — *p* — *f* — *p*

Den ed-len Mann ent-stellt die Ra - che, den ed-len

Belm. / Pedr. (B. P.) — *sotto voce* — *f* — *p* — *f* — *p*

A wor-thy man de-spis- es ven- geance, a wor-thy.

Andante sostenuto.

fp — *fp* — *fp*

C. Bl. — *f* — *p* — *f* — *p* — *f*

Mann entstellt die Ra - che, den ed-len Mann ent-stellt die

B. P. — *f* — *p* — *f* — *p* — *f*

man de-spis -es ven- -geance, a wor-thy man de-spis- -es

fp — *fp* — *f*

C. Bl. — *p*

Ra-che, gross-müthig, menschlich, gü - tig sein, und oh-ne Ei - gen-nutz ver-

B. P. — *p*

ven-geance, but to be mer— ci-ful and kind and to for-give with o- -pen-

p

C. Bl. — *cresc.* — *f*

zeih'n, ist nur der gro - ssen, der gro - ssen See - len Sa - - - -

B. P. — *cresc.* — *f*

mind, that is the no - ble, the no - ble spir - it's call - - - - -

cresc. — *f* — *fp*

Andante come prima.
Const.
all four
Alle vier.
Wer dieses nicht er-ken-nen kann, den seh man mit Ver-achtung an.
che.
ing.
He who this mor-al can for-get, shall with disdain and scorn be met.
Wer dieses
ing.
He who this
nicht er-ken-nen kann, den seh' man mit Ver-ach-tung an, den seh' man
mor-al can for-get, shall with dis-dain and scorn be met, shall with dis-
Allegro vivace.
mit Ver-ach-tung an.
dain and scorn be met.

Chorus of the Janissaries

CHOR der Janitscharen.

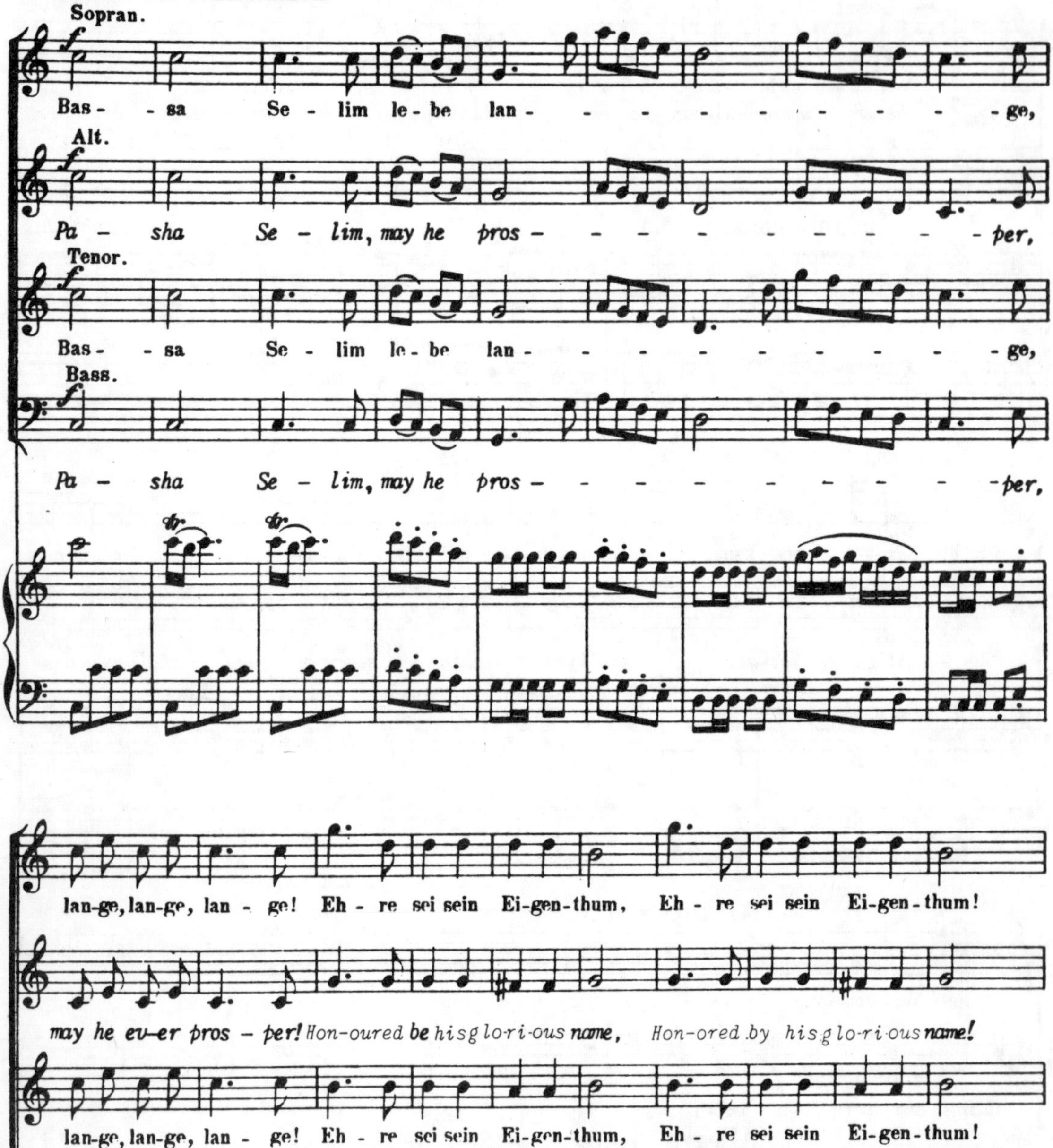
Sopran.
Bas - sa Se - lim le - be lan - - - - - - - - - - - ge,
Alt.
Pa - sha Se - lim, may he pros - - - - - - - - - - - per,
Tenor.
Bas - sa Se - lim le - be lan - - - - - - - - - - - ge,
Bass.
Pa - sha Se - lim, may he pros - - - - - - - - - - - per,
tr
tr
lan-ge, lan-ge, lan - ge! Eh - re sei sein Ei-gen-thum, Eh - re sei sein Ei-gen-thum!
may he ev-er pros - per! Hon-oured be his glo-ri-ous name, Hon-ored by his glo-ri-ous name!
lan-ge, lan-ge, lan - ge! Eh - re sei sein Ei-gen-thum, Eh - re sei sein Ei-gen-thum!
may he ev-er pros - per! Hon-oured be his glo-ri ous name, Hon-ored be his glo-ri-ous name!
tr
tr
tr
tr
p

Sei-ne hol-de Stirn um-schwebe Ju-bel, Freu-de, Glück und Ruhm, Jubel, Freu-de, Glück und
Ev-er proudly we shall hail him and his no-ble vir-tue's fame, and his no-ble vir-tue's
Sei-ne hol-de Stirn um-schwebe Ju-bel, Freu-de, Glück und Ruhm, Jubel, Freu-de, Glück und
Ev-er proudly we shall hail him and his no-ble vir-tue's fame, and his no-ble vir-tue's
Ruhm, Bassa Selim glücklich le-be, Eh-re sei sein Eigen-thum, Eh-re sei sein Eigen-thum,
fame. Pa-sha Selim may he prosper, honoured be his glo-ri-ous name honoured be his glo-ri-ous name.
Ruhm, Bassa Selim glücklich le-be, Eh-re sei sein Eigen-thum, Eh-re sei sein Eigen-thum,
fame. Pa-sha Selim may he prosper, honoured be his glo-ri-ous name, honoured his glo-ri-ous name.
und sein ho-her Scheitel pran-ge voll von Ju-bel und von Ruhm, voll von Ju-bel und von
Ev-er proudly we shall hail him, and his no-ble virtue's fame, and his no-ble vir-tue's
und sein ho-her Scheitel pran-ge voll von Ju-bel und von Ruhm, voll von Ju-bel und von
Ev-er proudly we shall hail him, and his no-ble virtue's fame, and his no-ble vir-tue's

Ruhm! Bassa Selim le-be lan-ge, Ehre sei sein Eigen-thum, Ehre sei sein Eigen-thum!
fame! Pa-sha Selim may he prosper, honoured be his glo-ri-ous name honoured be his glo-ri-ou name!
Ruhm! Bassa Selim le-be lan-ge, Ehre sei sein Eigen-thum, Ehre sei sein Eigen-thum!
fame! Pa-sha Selim may he prosper, honoured be his glo-ri-ous name honoured his glo-ri-ous name,
Bas- - sa Se - lim le - be lan- - - - - - - - - - - - - ge,
Pa - sha Se - lim, may he pros - - - - - - - - - - - per,
Bas- - sa Se - lim le - be lan- - - - - - - - - - - - ge,
Pa - sha Se - lim, may he pros - - - - - - - - - - - per,
lange, lange, lan - ge! Eh - re sei sein Ei-gen-thum, Eh - re sei sein Ei-gen-thum,
ev-er may he pros-per! Hon-oured be his glo-ri-ous name, Hon-oured be his glo-ri-ous name!
lange, lange, lan - ge! Eh - re sei sein Ei-gen-thum, Eh - re sei sein Ei-gen-thum,
ev-er may he pros-per! Hon-oured be his glo-ri-ous name, Hon-oured be his glo-ri-ous name!

Ende der Oper.
(End of the Opera)

OPERA

In English

ARGENTO	THE BOOR THE MASQUE OF ANGELS
BARAB	CHANTICLEER A GAME OF CHANCE
BEESON	THE SWEET BYE AND BYE
BENJAMIN	PRIMA DONNA A TALE OF TWO CITIES
BRITTEN	ALBERT HERRING BILLY BUDD A MIDSUMMER NIGHT'S DREAM PETER GRIMES THE RAPE OF LUCRETIA THE TURN OF THE SCREW
COPLAND	THE TENDER LAND
FLOYD	THE SOJOURNER AND MOLLIE SINCLAIR SUSANNAH WUTHERING HEIGHTS
HOIBY	NATALIA PETROVNA
MARTINU	COMEDY ON THE BRIDGE
MOORE	THE DEVIL AND DANIEL WEBSTER
STRAVINSKY	THE RAKE'S PROGRESS